SPORTS AND SOCIAL

SPORTS AND SOCIAL

Kevin Boniface

Bluemoose

For Mum,
the original Owl Lady,
1946–2022

Copyright © Kevin Boniface 2023

First published in 2023 by
Bluemoose Books Ltd
25 Sackville Street
Hebden Bridge
West Yorkshire
HX7 7DJ

www.bluemoosebooks.com

British Library Cataloguing-in-Publication data
A catalogue record for this book is available from the British Library

Paperback 978-1-915693-11-2

Printed and bound in the UK by Short Run Press

Contents

World of Interiors

The man with the short back and sides, whose shirt collars are pinching, is sitting in my seat on the train, so I sit in front of the woman with long black hair and purple eye shadow. She's speaking loudly into her phone.

"If I ever see Rachel Bradley again I swear I'll give her a right slap. She took the only thing I had left; the necklace with the garnets he bought me ... oxidised silver, kind of leafy? ... When I got home she'd left. She'd taken it with her ... It was like *I knew* she would have? ... I knew she'd been going into my room nicking stuff ... Well somebody had and I knew she'd had her eye on it. I'd caught her snooping around a couple of times ... I don't really want to go into it now but me and Stewart had something really special. It wasn't easy for me when we broke up."

Another man with a short back and sides drags a kit bag along the narrow aisle. He has a glowing tan and a t-shirt that says *Legendary* in an arc of Gothic lettering across the chest. He takes out his headphones to tell me I'm in his seat. He shows me his reservation: 22A. I tell him about the other man with the short back and sides who is in my seat and ask whether he needs seat 22A specifically as I've just stowed my things and will have to move everything. Half the seats in the carriage are empty. He sighs and rolls his eyes. Then the slim grey haired woman in the seat in front points out that he's read the numbers wrong anyway, 22A is the seat next to her. She stands up to let the Legendary man in. She has nice earrings.

The woman behind me is still on her phone.

"He could always make me laugh, you know? … My rat got out of its cage and the cat got it. I was gutted … So was my rat."

We stop at Grantham and two men in denim jackets get on the train. They sit opposite the woman with the earrings and the Legendary man with the table between them. In the reflection of the window I can see them all. None of them speak. The Legendary man is flicking through his phone and the others are avoiding eye contact. One of the denim jacket men is sitting very straight and rummaging through the bag on his knee, the other is fidgeting, tapping on the table and scratching himself.

The woman behind me is still on her phone.

"I'm not religious but there's a spirit in Market Weighton that doesn't like me".

Another phone rings. A man in a black pinstripe suit answers.

"I'm going to kill you, mate … It's a nightmare, it's Hell on earth … I can't talk now but there's a woman on her phone behind me and she's driving me mad … Ages mate, hours … Everything … I'll tell you when I get there … It's a nightmare. *And I'm going backwards!* See you in a bit, mate … Thanks. Bye bye."

The woman is still on her phone.

"No, but there's this thing, um, spontaneous human combustion? When a human being just bursts into flames? And I *definitely* believe in that, I mean, it's happened, no one can deny it, there are photographs. No one knows why. They've done research but they can't work it out but I definitely believe in it … Kurt Cobain was murdered … there are too many weird things? Like the gun was in his right hand and he was left-handed …"

A man with his name on a badge (Peter Robinson) is pushing a refreshment trolley down the aisle when a bald man with wire rimmed glasses, who has been reading the Daily Mail while his wife flicks through a magazine, calls him over and asks for a can of Carslberg. The bald man hands Peter Robinson some coins, leans forward and says quietly,

"Can't you shut that woman up?"

"She going on a bit, is she sir?" says Peter Robinson with a chuckle.

The bald man nods sternly and opens his lager.

"Like there are these four or five people who basically run the world ... There is not a single scrap or even the tiniest weeniest shred of evidence to prove that covid even exists ..."

The bald man with the lager and the Daily Mail twists around to get a look at the phone woman and his wife puts her hand on his knee and whispers something to him. He whispers something back that starts with "Well!" and sinks back in his seat with his beer.

When we pull into Kings Cross everyone in the carriage stands up and turns to get a look at the phone woman. She doesn't notice, she's still on the phone.

Outside the station, the streets of London are lined with smokers and vapers of all ages. A group of brightly coloured students huddle around the base of a pillar and a man with a dogtooth flat cap and Pringle pullover offers me a leaflet with some information about God's love. I lean against a wall and roll myself a cigarette.

I set off in what I think is the direction of Clerkenwell. I was going to buy some lunch on the way but after a half mile or so all I've passed are a couple of square concrete pubs, the frontages of which are propped up with more smokers who stand their beer on window ledges while they swear at one another. I double back to the station and buy a disappointing sandwich then I phone Edgar to see if he's in town yet.

Edgar meets me at a pub on Farringdon Road. He's wearing his dark grey trilby and the heavy woollen overcoat that's always looked a bit big on him. He's carrying an umbrella and has a big camera bag over his shoulder. We shake hands and decide to sit outside. I have a coffee and Edgar has tea. People who speak like Edgar walk past quickly. They do everything quickly, with tippy-tappy shoes. Motorists all drive so quickly that the traffic hardly moves and the cyclists ride quickly through the gaps.

After our drinks we head back to the station. I follow Edgar down some escalators to the underground. We stand near a woman in a bright red coat and a man in skinny jeans who is reading a thick paperback. There are some girls speaking a foreign language. A man in an old Adidas tracksuit is working his way along the platform asking for money. On the edge of the platform, I recognise the woman from the train. She's fiddling with her phone, frustrated with the lack of signal. The train blows into the station and the phone woman takes a step backwards. The draught blows her long hair into the face of one of the foreign girls who spits it out of her mouth and flaps it away with her hand. The phone woman doesn't notice, she's put a finger in her ear and is shouting into the receiver as the train clatters to a halt.

On the train, I stare up at the network map above the hand straps and count the number of stops. Edgar takes off his hat and rests it on his lap. He tells me Dorothy can't wait to see me. She's at home preparing roast lamb. We talk about the exhibition. Edgar tells me he's read an article about it in the paper and says he's looking forward to it.

4

We change onto the overground train at Victoria and as we pass through Brixton station Edgar points out the life size bronze statues of people waiting for trains on the platform. He says he likes to think of the statues wandering off for a break during quiet spells and reconvening whenever anybody arrives.

A group of school children get on the train and sit opposite us. They throw sweets at each other and share headphones. Edgar tells me a story about a schoolboy who decapitated himself.

"He got up to look out of one of the old push-down windows and a couple of seconds later his headless body collapsed on the floor of the carriage." Edgar says he's heard and told the story so many times he sometimes feels as though he witnessed it himself.

We alight and make the short walk to Edgar and Dorothy's through the splayed suburbs of wide streets and sticky lime trees. The traffic noise is background and sedate. I can hear children playing, birdsong even. A young man with a neat moustache is shakily circumnavigating the roundabout on an electric scooter with both of his indicators flashing at once. He completes three circuits before he finally manages to take his turn-off.

"Sorry, mate!" he yells as he narrowly misses the man in the sensible brown shoes who is dragging bundles of the Evening Standard from the back of a van while singing.

"Roll-up, bowl a ball, a penny a pitch."

The sky is grey and arcs overhead unimpeded by tall buildings. We turn off the main road into a broad, well-maintained street, cars parked half on wide pavements. Neat gardens roll out below the two storey bay windows of each redbrick and pebbledash terrace house.

Edgar flicks the latch of the shiny black wooden gate and it swings open easily. It clicks shut behind me as I follow him up the rope edged crazy paving to the black front door with the oval leaded light panel. I can smell the food inside. Dorothy opens the door in a stripy pinny over one of her turquoise long sleeved dresses and knocks off her glasses giving me a big kiss.

After dinner she tells me she's made up a bed for me on the unusually convex mattress in the dark back bedroom that gave my sister nightmares when she was young. The room is cluttered with wooden masks and figurines from Zambia and India. There are black and white photographs of relatives aboard ships posing with pulleys and ropes, wearing pith helmets under a banyan tree, playing a euphonium for an audience of elephants. There are yellowing paperbacks: Insects in Colour, The Fontana Wild Flower Guide, The Honey and Cider-Vinegar Way to Health, Gray's Anatomy Descriptive and Applied, Battle for the Mind, The Mechanics of Indoctrination, Brainwashing and Thought Control. I hang my shirt on the decorative wooden spear of a Bantu tribesman and get into bed.

In the morning Edgar and I head back into town to the exhibition. We get off the bus and find somewhere for lunch. Edgar takes me to a café he used to frequent when he worked in town. The proprietor is a big stereotype Italian man with red and yellow smears down his white apron who speaks loudly and has a pencil behind his ear. He recognises Edgar and they shake hands warmly. There are sun bleached light box photographs of lasagna and meat balls dusted with flaky parmesan. I have panini.

At the gallery, the rooms are spotless and brightly lit. The ceilings are high and ornate. A man in his forties primps his fastidiously unkempt hairstyle in the reflection of one of the huge glass panels that divide the larger spaces. Young people with lank hair and wine-stained hoodies mingle with older people in brown pinstripes or tweeds with brooches, their heads tilted back as they peer at the exhibits through varifocals. The older men have pens in their pockets and I hear one of the older women ask someone whether they would like a lozenge.

Half the work is hung on the white walls, half is arranged on the parquet floor with ropes around it.

I spend the afternoon at the exhibition trying to take notes that sound as though I might have some insight into something while Edgar goes for a wander with his camera.

In a side-room off the main gallery there's an installation entitled World of Interiors. It's a re-creation of a bedroom in which, according to the foam-board statement by the door frame, *Every item down to the smallest hair clip and discarded paper tissue is replaced with an exact replica every day for the duration of the exhibition.* The room is slightly shabby; lilac woodchip walls pocked with blu-tac/drawing pin scars, a dog-eared poster of William Blake's Whirlwind of Lovers from Dante's Inferno. Tulles and organzas have been draped from the ceiling. There are candles, books of Romantic poetry, biographies of dead rock stars. Lover's Guide DVDs share a Contiboard bookcase with a dragon's skull ornament, a pair of brass chalices and leather and beaded jewellery featuring yins, yangs, ankhs, Celtic knots and pentagrams. There are soft toys, pens, marbles, and flyers for concerts by bands whose members looked like wizards. There are bangles, neckerchiefs, phone accessories featuring skull and crossbones motifs. There's an old PC monitor which has been painted with red emulsion. There are art postcards, Millais' Ophelia, Dali's Crucifixion, more William Blake. There's a tie-dyed bedspread, an adjustable tailor's dummy with an oxidised silver and garnet necklace around its neck and there are photographs in plastic snakeskin frames by the head of the bed. I look closer at the people in the pictures, mainly taken in nightclubs, their faces bleached by flash bulbs. I'm struck by one of them, she features a lot; it's the phone woman from the train. I lean in as close as I can. *It is.* I go back to the printed statement by the door frame: World of Interiors, Rachel Bradley and Stewart Marshall.

Body Heat

It's cold. I push my specs up the bridge of my nose so I can see better to burn off the untidy straggles of tobacco from the tip of my too tightly rolled cigarette, then I turn left over the railway bridge and out onto the main road, where I pass a group of teenage boys.

"I wa' sat in t' front room at 'alf four in t' morning drinking neat vodka."

"Wa' ya?"

"Yeh, I wa' rocking backward and for'ard on t'settee an' all that."

"Fuckin' 'ell!"

In the queue at the bus stop I stand behind a woman who looks like she probably looks older than she is.

"Good it's come nice for the weekend. Better than all that rain we've been having."

Over the road, vapour rises as the Jack Russell terrier pisses against the big toe of the enormous sunny orange bikini girl airbrushed to the side of the Body Heat fairground ride in the car park of the Craven Heifer. The dog's owner, an elderly man in a frayed Harrington jacket, gazes up at an enormous pair of starburst breasts.

The bus squeals to the kerb and I flick the remains of my rubbish cigarette down a storm drain and find a seat by a nearside window. My twenty minute ride takes in the majority of the town's builders' wholesalers and motor factors before I alight at the bus stop outside the new Penthouse Gentlemen's Club: bits of plastic chrome and smoked glass fastened to the front of a dilapidated nineteenth century former brewery.

I head across the road and through the yard of newish silver cars where I reattach the vinyl banner which has slipped its moorings in the night again: *A great selection of top quality vehicles for personal and business use.* In the far corner of the yard, at the prefab office with the all-year round swollen door, I twist the handle as far as it'll go and lean heavily on it with my full weight to make sure the latch is clear of the lock. Then I simultaneously shoulder and kick the door free of its frame. It shudders open violently, triggering the electronic bell which, before the rain got into the unit, reminded me of the beginning of the Colonel Bogey March. Inside the office, the plug-in electric heater has already steamed up the windows and there are puddles of condensation on the sills below. This is a persistent problem at this time of the year and, some time ago, in order to try and solve it, I'd taken the saucer from under the spider plant that just about lived on the windowsill in the corner nearest the hinged section of the mahogany formica counter. I'd hoped the plant might soak up some of the water and stop it dripping onto the carpet below but it's never really worked. The carpet is still permanently sodden in the winter and when it eventually dries out each summer the tidemark reaches a bit further into the centre of the room. The plant has thrived though, nobody has ever watered it but it has tripled in size. Half of its variegated leaves are stuck fast to the windowpane and its leggy runners dangle from the sill and into the wastepaper basket on the floor below.

I force the door back into its frame, cross to the counter where I sweep two spent tea bags into the bin with the palm of my hand and lift the counter top.

"Morning," I call into the back.

"Morning," says Irfan who is booting up the computer. He leans away and points to a mug of tea with a picture of some spark plugs on it, I pick it up and dump my bag on the chair.

"Cheers, mate."

The morning passes off uneventfully. I deal with the paperwork and Irfan with the customers, it's a division of labour that has evolved over several years. Irfan is a natural communicator, confident and friendly. I'm not. He also looks the part in his suit and chisel toes; he rarely wears the same silk tie twice.

At half-past twelve I go to get lunch. I eschew our usual sandwich shop and walk the extra quarter of a mile up to the big supermarket. It was Irfan's idea.

"I can't be doing with all that cardboard shit, It's Saturday, I'm gonna treat myself, get us one of them fancy wrap things."

I get held up in the gravy aisle. Ashley Betts and his elderly mother are blocking the way while they argue about stuffing.

"I'm not eating that," says Ashley. His thin bleached blond hair slipping to reveal the extent of his receding hairline. He's wearing a short-sleeved shirt; cream with a narrow green stripe which compliments a pink tank top and a pair of 1980s style bleached jeans. His mother wears her hair in a tight grey perm and has a pair of chunky dark-rimmed glasses pushed down her nose. Her old gabardine trench coat falls below the knee and is teamed with opaque tights and a pair of colourful Nike Air Max. She's holding a cardboard packet of stuffing mix in her hand.

"*You* might not want to eat it but what about everyone else?" she says.

"You'll have to cook mine separately, I'm not having that stuff anywhere near my dinner."

"Don't be so silly," says his mother leaning forward to put the stuffing mix in the trolley. Ashley jerks the trolley away from her hand.

"I'm not having it," he says again through clenched teeth. "It'll be like when we were in the Isle of White, remember? Mine came out with stuffing on and it all went back, the whole lot, didn't it?"

"Yes," says his mother, "you could have just left it on one side."

Ashley leans forward "I'm not touching it."
His mother tosses the stuffing into the trolley and they move off bickering into the Healthy Meals aisle.

I've not seen Ashley Betts for ages; he was a couple of years above me at school and I've hardly seen him since. He could never say his Rs properly and he wore his brother's hand-me-down Ocean Pacific sweatshirt until it fell apart. I thought about saying hello but decided against it.

I buy lunch and set off back to the yard. I wait at the crossing next to two women.

"What do you reckon?" asks the one next to me with the dyed pink hair and the Blondie t-shirt featuring a screen-printed headshot of Debbie Harry.

"I reckon you do right. Just go in and tell them. What harm's it gonna do?" replies her companion: long naturally blonde hair, no fringe, black billowing outfit in jersey.

I'm pretty sure I recognise the second woman's voice.

"I'll just go in and tell them," says the Blondie fan. "I'll just go in and I'll just say 'Every time I come in this shop I get a right belt off them trolleys.'"

I lean forward to try and get a discreet look at her companion while the Blondie fan is talking.

"I'll tell them. Sometimes I daren't even touch them 'cause I know I'm gonna get a shock."

She mimes getting a static shock from a shopping trolley, 'Eeurggharghh!' She leans back and waves her arms in the air to simulate her discomfort and I get a clear view of the other woman. I *did* recognise her voice, It's Charmaine Walker. I haven't seen *her* for years either.

The Blondie fan is still going on, "It's putting me off going into the shop for Christ's sake! I'm definitely gonna tell em" she says again.

"You do right," reiterates Charmaine.

The lights change and everyone crosses the road. I'm a bit flustered. I've not seen Charmaine for ages but I remember the last time I did very clearly. I say nothing and hurry past with my head down.

I shift the fleece jackets and carrier bags from the chair in the corner of the office and sit down to eat. I tear my cheese sandwich into bite-sized pieces and slip a couple of plain crisps between the slices of each piece before eating them one at a time, sometimes leaving the crusts. Irfan always says I'm obsessive with food. He sits on the desk with his feet on the edge of the chair which he rocks forwards onto two legs. He balances it like this for a while until it suddenly flips forward, catching his shin as it falls. He leans forward, rights the chair and tries again. This time he balances it as far forwards as he dares before pushing it back at the last second before it falls. Simultaneously he eats the wrap from which he hasn't bothered to remove much of the packaging. Occasionally he pulls pieces of cardboard and plastic from his mouth and wipes them on a paper serviette on the edge of the desk. When he's finished, he wipes his mouth and looks at me.

"I'm not still covered in crap, am I?"

I point to my own top lip to indicate where Irfan still has residue soured cream in his neatly sculpted moustache.

Between nibbling at my food, I tell Irfan about seeing my old school friends in town.

"Do you reckon I should have spoken to them?"

"No," he answers assuredly, and he reminds me about an incident a few months ago. Another old friend of mine had been in to hire a car. He said he needed it to take his mum up to Robin Hood's Bay for the weekend and I'd given him a big mates' rate discount. The police found the car two weeks later in a car park at Manchester airport and there's been no sign of him since.

"You're a bloody soft touch you are," says Irfan. "I'd stay well away from your mental mates if I were you. They are MEN-TAL! And they take the piss."

I concede that Irfan might have a point and explain the circumstances of my last meeting with Charmaine. Charmaine and I had started going out when we were both fifteen. We stayed together after school and went through sixth form. After that, I got a place at university in Leeds doing music and she got a job at a firm of local travel agents.

"Hold up! You went to college?" says Irfan losing control of the chair again.

"It was a music degree so, you know?" I explain. "Anyway, Leeds wasn't far away and we were gonna stay together, you know?" I roll the sticker off my apple and flick it across the room, "But the week before my course started we went to a party at a mate's house. I went up for a piss late on, and there she was, on the bed with him." I bite into the apple. "So, I reckon you're right, they take the piss."

"See," says Irfan, "you're best off out of it, man."

We're interrupted by the noise of somebody wrestling with the door of the office. It eventually rattles open and sets off the water damaged Colonel Bogey. Irfan leans back on the desk, stretches himself and goes to deal with the customer.

I clear the crumbs and packaging and spend the rest of the afternoon filing, avoiding creditors and having a couple of cigarette breaks.

It's Saturday, so Irfan leaves early in his sunglasses and immaculate Golf GTi. I lock up the yard and walk into town. I want to get some food before I meet the others for Chris's fortieth do. Chris Maguire is another old mate. I met him through a mutual college friend, Dan who played fiddle in a crusty folk band called Blackjack Davy and the Dogs. Dan wore knitwear and unusual hats, as did Chris, as on occasions did I, though I was never as committed to the cause as the others. A few of Chris's circle were, and still are members of the War of the Roses re-enactment society. I'd maybe catch the end of *Time Team* if it was on, that's as far as it ever went for me.

I end up at the chip shop and decide to sit in and eat off the formica. I find a small table in the lee of an enormous tower of Coke cans, overlooked only by a laminated Pukka Pie poster featuring a young couple sharing a steak pie in bed. *ALL STEAK: a full filling experience.* I pick at the fish, cutting off small morsels and trying each with a different condiment in order: ketchup, mushy peas and vinegar, tartare sauce, salad cream, ketchup, mushy peas and vinegar, tartare sauce, salad cream, ketchup, mushy peas and vinegar, tartare sauce, salad cream ... The table is littered with portion control detritus of all hues.

I leave as the evening is drawing in and make my way up through town to The Ship Inn where I've arranged to meet Dan and a few other friends in their outdoor sherpa woollens. We have a couple of drinks; we mainly reminisce about mohair and discuss camper van parts and then we share a taxi out to the suburban church hall where Chris's party is being held.

Balloons flutter and bob from the eaves. Above them, a big homemade banner: CHRIS MAGUIRE 40. Belinda Carlisle's *Heaven is a Place on Earth* soft-rocks out from the open doors. It's early yet and the venue is sparsely populated, just a couple of children in pin-striped waistcoats on the dance floor. In the corner, a trestle table bows under the weight of an enormous garden muck tub filled with cans of Red Stripe, bottles of spirits and iced water. Next to this is a couple of dozen cans of bitter, some fancy IPAs and a two litre jug of orange juice which is nearly empty. On the opposite side of the hall, DJ Jitters has set up his Souvenir Roadshow on another trestle and is playing The Best Music From The Fifties To Today's Chart Hits according to the hand stencilled white lettering on the old blackout curtain he's hung on the wall behind him. I take a can of lager and go outside into the graveyard for a roll-up.

"You need some wacky baccy before you go back in there, don't you?" shouts one of the women from a group huddled under the hawthorn tree on the other side of the path. I laugh politely as a blonde woman comes out of the hall behind me dressed in a billowing lightweight trouser suit in turquoise with a matching chiffon scarf. It's Charmaine! She doesn't see me. She has a cigarette pursed between her lips while she fumbles around in the bottom of her handbag. She pulls out a lighter, lights up and calls over to the wacky-baccy woman under the tree who greets her enthusiastically.

"Charmaine! I didn't realise you were here!" They go into a huddle and the wacky-baccy woman fills Charmaine in on some news.

"Did you hear about Bob? He's been offered some voluntary work at the armouries. It's ever so exciting."

I wander off as casually as I can and hide behind a large memorial stone. I smoke my cigarette and then decide to make an attempt to sneak back into the hall to join Dan and the others but the wacky-baccy woman sees me,

"I bet you're ready for anything now, aren't you?" she shouts.

Charmaine's jaw drops. "Fucking hell, I don't *believe* it!"

"Hi Charmaine," I say.

Charmaine gathers herself "Bloody hell! I haven't seen you for years."

The church hall door opens again and *It's a Love Thing* floods out: The look in your eyes is more than enough to make my poor heart burst into flames.

A silhouette of a man props open the door with his foot while he leans on the frame and jokes to somebody inside above the loud music.

"Fuck off! You wanna be careful mate, people'll talk." He steps outside and lets the door swing shut behind him, "Charmaine! I've been looking for you," he says.

It's Ashley Betts in a long sleeved Helly Hansen T-shirt stretched over his paunch and a vintage Nokia N95 swinging from a lanyard around his neck. He sees me.

"Fuck me! Long time no see."

"Hi Ashley," I say.

"Blimey, it's been years! Hey, don't you go getting any ideas about my missus either, you're not in Mrs Charlesworth's storeroom now!"

Ashley reminisces keenly about school. I mainly nod and occasionally push my specs up the bridge of my nose. I feel uncomfortable, I feel whatever the opposite of nostalgic is. Charmaine smiles a lot but doesn't say much. Eventually, as the evening cools and glasses are drained, we all head back inside to get more drinks and find a table. Charmaine and Ashley update me on the years I've missed. They got together while reenacting the Battle of Bosworth Field in 2001 and have been married fifteen years last Saturday. Charmaine was Cecily Duchess of York in a wimple and some curtains and Ashley was an archer with a longbow and a set of complicated instructions. They live in a barn conversion in the Peak District from where Ashley directs operations at the chain of bakery retailers he established in the late nineties. It's been a lot of hard work and long hours and Ashley feels he deserves the Porsche 911 he drives. His pasties are well thought of, "Probably the best in the Yorkshire Region" and he's got asymmetrical engraved glass trophies from the Yorkshire Post Taste Awards 2004 *and* 2015 to prove it. Charmaine is his secretary and his rock. They hold hands.

I've drunk several cans of lager when I'm pulled from my seat and onto the dance floor by Dan and Chris. Chris is wearing a plastic tiara and a green hi-visibility vest with a drawing of a handgun and Maggers P.I. written across the back in black marker pen. We dance boisterously to *I Believe In A Thing Called Love* by The Darkness, until DJ Jitters stops it half way through. Jitters lost his patience when Chris bumped into his trestle for a third time and upset half a can of Red Stripe and a cardboard plate of Mini-Rolls. Inevitably Dan gets into an argument with DJ Jitters and his girlfriend has to intervene. Chris says it's just like the old days and I roll my eyes without really thinking.

"What's that supposed to fucking mean you miserable bastard!" Chris blows up. "You always were a miserable cunt!" He swings a drunken punch which glances the side of my face and I fall backwards into Jitters's trestle table. Jitters shoves me away from his decks and I land prone on the dance floor. Dan leaps on Jitters and a brawl develops. Several of the other guests step in and attempt to calm things. Ashley springs into the ruck, arms out, palms down.

"Come on lads, let's save it for the battlefield. Calm down!"

I gather up the remains of my specs and get to my feet. I swipe a bottle of vodka from the muck tub and leave. Charmaine runs out after me but Ashley catches her by the arm.

"Come on, love. He'll be right."

I stumble around through the suburban estates of ex-council semis gulping back the vodka from the bottle. On, past the Motor Factors, the urban fox, a group of teenage boys.
"I wa' off me tits!"
"Wa' ya?"
"Yeh, they reckon it stays in your system forever!"

Somehow, I find my way back to the fairground at The Craven Heifer on the main road. I clamber over to one of the bucket seats of the Body Heat ride, crawl under the canvas cover and fall asleep there surrounded by airbrushed young women in small leather bikinis riding powerful American motorcycles.

Confusion

What I knew was that Matt did English Literature at university in Brighton in the mid 1980s. He met his wife Laura there. She was a music student. When they'd graduated, Laura got a good job teaching up here and they moved north. They bought a semi in Hagenby about five miles out of town. I thought I knew the road: you turn left after the market cross. I know it because there's this odd topiary carport about halfway down on the left. I think it's a cotoneaster, it's got red berries. It's huge. It's obviously been trained on an arch over the driveway at some point but the arch has gone and now it's just this weird topiary tunnel. The bloke who lives there parked an immaculate cherry red Rover 75 estate under it for years, but I don't think he's got it anymore. Anyway, as far as I knew Matt and Laura lived somewhere down there when Matt set up that culty sci-fi magazine of his, I can't remember what it was called, I'm not really into that sort of stuff. He used to supplement his income with bits and bats of other writing. He had a bit of a film review column in the local paper under a pseudonym at one point, David something.

Anyway, they (Matt and Laura) were both about forty by the time the twins came along. It was a *massive* blessing for Matt, he'd always wanted kids and he completely threw himself into it. He gave up a lot, you know? He sacrificed the freedom of his freelancing lifestyle and took the job at ours. He said he just needed a steady, reliable income.

Matt's girls were the same age as my youngest and when they were little we'd discuss the kids every morning, you know: weening, teething, first steps, school, swimming lessons, childcare, holiday logistics etc. All the stuff that people with young kids always bore you with. I got on with Matt, he was all right, he was definitely one of the more interesting blokes I've worked with. There was a bit more to him than just the usual football and beer.

Him and Laura used to be in this covers band, just local, you know. Anyway, it had gradually morphed into a proper New Order tribute act. I think they were both really into the Manchester thing. Matt was Bernard Sumner and Laura was usually Peter Hook but she could deputise as any of the others if she needed to because she was a proper musician. Matt said she even wore a fake moustache when she was being Hooky. He kept promising to send me an mp3, but he never did.

Matt was a funny looking bugger really, he was very much on the eccentric side looks wise. He wasn't a big lad, he was slight, I suppose he was quite skinny really. His clothes hung off him, they always seemed like they were much too big for him, as if he'd shrunk since he'd bought them. And he walked with this kind of limp, like a shuffle, with one foot splayed out. But the maddest thing was his hair. He had a proper Carry On combover, the full Bobby Charlton.

Anyway, more recently Matt's eccentricities clothes-wise had become a bit extreme. He was wearing the same torn trousers for days on end. They had this massive rip in them, he said he'd caught them on a fence. You could see his undies! He just carried on wearing them. And he had this shirt that had all blood down it from when he'd had a nosebleed, like *weeks* before. There were rumours going round that he'd started drinking heavily.

I'd heard he liked a drink, but folk were saying he'd got really bad with it.

Anyway, one day, it'll have been January last year, Matt came into work all excited. He told me the band had been booked to support this Iggy and the Stooges tribute act on a tour round Europe in the summer. His mum and dad had agreed to have the kids and he'd managed to blag a month off work. They were rehearsing three nights a week and they were planning this big summer getaway, a proper trip of a lifetime thing. He smartened himself up again. He was upbeat, and over the next few months he was going on about all their plans. They were hiring buses and booking trains and places to stay and all that. He'd even bought a load of phrase books.

So anyway, I'd pretty much forgotten about all the rumours about Matt's drinking because he seemed fine. He was back to normal, as normal as he ever was anyway! But then in about the April, I started to get a bit suspicious myself.

Because he didn't drive, I used to give him a lift out to his jobs and a couple of times I thought I could smell alcohol on him. Then, one morning I noticed this big two litre bottle in his bag, you know, one of them big two litre plastic jobs that cheap cider comes in. It wasn't cider though, it was clear, like water. I wasn't sure what it was. I suppose it could have been white cider or maybe vodka or, as Matt claimed, it could actually have just been water.

Another time, I went to drop his tools at the place where he was working and when I got there, there was no sign of him but there was vomit sprayed everywhere. It was all down the door and all over the floor of the customer's new bloody shed! The bloke came out and hosed it down. He wasn't angry with Matt, he liked him, everyone did. We all did. He *was* worried though and he said he'd try and have a word with him about it. Anyway, when I saw the bloke the next day, he told me Matt had said he'd just had a bit of a stomach bug and was feeling fine now. The bloke seemed to buy the story so so did I. But then, a few days later, Matt was very obviously *completely* wasted. It was when we went out to the yard for the van. He was staggering and slurring his words. It was proper weird, we'd been together all morning getting stuff organised and he'd been fine, then, when we were finished he'd nipped to the toilet while I went to fetch the keys for the van. A quarter of an hour later he reappeared, *completely* fucked. Anyway, this time I confronted him about it, I was quite angry about it actually, I felt like he'd let me down, it felt like he was playing me for an idiot. It was ridiculous, he was *so* pissed. I accused him of drinking. I told him he was in no fit state to be doing the job, it was dangerous more than anything, he was all over the place. He just laughed at me and slurred "I'm fine". He told me to chill. He said it was just some tablets he was on that he'd reacted badly to. He said it had happened before and the effects had worn off after a few minutes. In the end I just dropped him off as usual. I just thought well, *maybe* it's true and it's kind of up to him anyway so …

Anyway, a couple of hours later I got a phone call from my boss; can I go over to Matt's job and try and smooth things over? Matt had collapsed and they'd had to call an ambulance.

Matt was suspended from work. After a few days there were more rumours: "He's tried to come back, he just walked back in with all his gear as if nowt's happened," "He was in the yard again, he ended up brawling with that new boss, they had to physically throw him out." It was all a bit vague, a bit sketchy. Everyone was a bit cagey and tight-lipped. It was a bit of a sensitive situation and nobody wanted to incriminate or upset anybody.

Then we got the news that he'd died. It was a right shock. More information was drip, drip, dripping out and it turned out that another lad from work who lived near him had finally got him to admit to his drinking. Matt had been determined to kick the habit and get back to work so he'd just gone for it, cold turkey, and he never made it. It's awful, isn't it?

Anyway, the funeral; it was a right revelation. I found out that Matt hadn't lived on that estate in Haganby at all, he'd been living with his disabled mother, he always had done ever since his dad had died fifteen years before. He'd never lived with a partner, he'd *never* been married, *there was no such person as Laura*. He'd *never* had kids. All that stuff we used to talk about! He must have just made it up. It's mad, isn't it? He'd never been in a band; he'd never even played a musical instrument as far as anyone else knew. I don't know for sure about the English degree in Brighton or the sci-fi magazine and all that, I forgot to ask anyone about that. He'd made *everything* up and I just believed him, but why wouldn't you? I've no idea who he really was.

The Owl Ladies and the 1980s

Mum and her friends are all owls of some kind: Tawny Owl, Snowy Owl, Brown Owl et cetera; names given to all Brownie Guide leaders. They are serious about Guiding. On the windowsill, below the foggy perspex double glazing in our front room, there is a collection of ornamental owl figurines, few of which Mum has bought herself. Everyone buys owls for her to commemorate her long involvement in the Guide movement. I've done it myself more than once. She now has seven of the Girl Guide officially sanctioned Wade Whimsy Long-Eared Owls but she doesn't mind. They are spread all around the house in different rooms. There are two in the bathroom and one that sits in a homemade nest of shredded yellow tissue paper in a cranny in the inglenook fireplace. She has brass owls, paper maché owls (that Carol made at Craft Day in Gomersal), pottery owls, wax candle owls which will never be lit and the macramé owls which she made herself with a kit my sister got her from the Guide Shop in Leeds. Some of the larger owls have been damaged, usually by Dad moving unwieldy objects around the room too quickly. There's an owl clock, an owl Scraperfoil picture and a precious set of three owls from Poole Pottery that Dad bought for mum in Dorset when we went on a house swap holiday with a C of E minister from Hampreston. All Mum's friends have pretend owls in their houses too, Pam Liversedge (Snowy Owl to Mum's Brown) even helps out at a local sanctuary for real owls.

I think I need to mention the plastic cake stand, the whole plastic ensemble and the table too; it's mainly beige plastic, pretend wickerwork, but it has chocolate brown metal tubular legs. There's this integral cake stand attachment and also a parasol/umbrella thing but we hardly ever use that. We *do* use the cake stand though. Dad will come out onto the patio where Mum will be chairing a meeting of the Divisional County Pack Holiday Advisors and he'll be there in his white satiné running shorts with navy blue bias binding, an old pair of Jesus sandals and a frayed tea towel over his shoulder. He'll use the cake stand for a coffee and walnut cake with butter icing. They'll all be sat round the table, Mum's friends and colleagues who are all called things like Linda, Pam (you know, from Gomersal), Christine, Eileen, Jean, Barbara, Susan, Carol, Pat et cetera and so on. They'll probably take the opportunity to compare notes on their 'sins' with photocopied Slimming World diet sheets. Pam's the only one who actually goes to the meetings; she tells the others what to do and then photocopies the notes for them. And Dad will cut the cake on the plastic wickerwork cake stand and flirt a bit by doing quite a good Frankie Howerd impression. Mum will be a bit embarrassed, but her friends and colleagues will laugh, apart from maybe Carol. There's always a lot of navy blue around that table and a lot of sensible shoes underneath it.

Alan Gledhill is the husband of Pat. Pat's all right, she's the funniest of Mum's friends. A few years ago she had quite a tight perm but Alan's was tighter. Anyway, Alan was tall, slim and blond, and he had quite a tight perm, like I said. He also wore a gold cygnet ring and neck chain and he smoked a lot of cigarettes; people did in those days. Once, he and Pat were at one of those parents and teachers versus the kids sports evenings at school. It was in the summer and there were clouds of midges. Dad, Mum and most of Mum's friends were there, watching the kids versus the parents netball game. My sister was in the kids' team and Mum's friend Barbara (Pat's Snowy

Owl) was captain of the parents' team. Barbara was a former member of the England national team, so it all got a bit one sided in the end.

Mum and Dad bought their house from Barbara and her husband John. John is a builder and he built it. Between them, Barbara and John are responsible for the eccentric wiring, the sunken bath, the patio doors, the wall-to-wall floor-to-ceiling mirrors in the bedrooms and the name Meadow View; all things that my dad has never really been happy with but has never got round to doing anything about. He did, however, double glaze the front room with some lengths of oak effect moulding and big panels of clear perspex.

One of the features established by Barbara and John that Dad and Mum do make good use of is the pretend marble breakfast bar. Mum eats her Cambridge Diet pretend chocolate (like soggy Texan bars but with less sugar) and Dad eats his Breakfast Slice (a bit like bacon but with more sugar). They sit there together and flick through what's left of the local paper; Dad will have used most of it to soak up a spillage from the dog's water bowl which he trips over most mornings. Dad also used to make good use of John's old garage wall mounted cupboard in pretend walnut veneer. He stored dozens of cartons of Asda fruit juice in and on top of it until it inevitably fell off the wall and damaged the paintwork of the Mini.

Once a month, Mum and Dad drive to the Asda in Sheffield in the Mini to stock up our garage-based chest freezer with own-brand products. Sometimes Dad drives the Mini to one of the villages in the foothills of the Peak District, there's a cake shop up there and he says it's the only place you can buy decent Eccles cakes. He phones ahead to order a hundred at a time and brings them back for the freezer.

On the touchline at the netball game at the school sports evening, Dad was dressed as a crude stereotype of an elderly woman ready for the football match. He'd decided to dress like this because the last time he took part he felt his teammates had taken the whole thing much too seriously. On one occasion Jeremy Benson's Dad had refused to pass the ball to him because Dad had deliberately given the ball away in comic fashion for a third time and the kids' team, my team, had gone on to score a goal as a result. So, Dad was there, watching the netball in a long synthetic bob, smeared pink lipstick, a floral 'old-lady' dress with balloons underneath for breasts, and a pair of football boots. Dad was serious about undermining seriousness.

Like I said, Alan and Pat were watching the netball too. Alan was wearing his man's clothes and his tight perm. Their daughter, Debbie was also in the kids' netball team. Alan and Pat had two daughters; Julie who was eldest had recently gone up to high school. Alan, along with my Dad, was one of the few dads who regularly got involved with school activities although he never really said much. Most of the kids in the netball team were either sisters, daughters or nieces of members or former members of either Mum's, Barbara's or Pat's Brownie Guide packs.

So, there we all were on the touchline of the junior school netball court, Alan, Pat, Mum and Dad, all the navy blue Owl Ladies and me. It was a warm evening and there were clouds of midges. Alan was smoking and Mum went over and stood next to him saying she'd heard cigarette smoke keeps midges away. Ordinarily Mum can't abide cigarettes. She and Dad have often spoken out against them, they even sent two of their closest smoker friends, Christine and Keith, photographs of a diseased lung through the post. Mum is a nurse and proud to be able to access such material.

Alan was there, smoking, and when Mum came over and stood next to him, laughing and clinging on to his arm under his smoky midge umbrella, he looked uneasy and bashful. He seemed quite shy generally and rarely spoke, but on the occasions he did he'd elicit shrieks of laughter from all the Owl Ladies which seemed to both excite and embarrass him. Anyway, just then, Miss Aberdeen who was refereeing the netball game screamed out in pain. She'd collided with a player from the parents' team and dislocated her thumb. She came running over to the touchline, her thumb badly misshapen. Dad, who has some first aid experience, briefly inspected the injury before grasping Miss Aberdeen's wrist firmly in his left hand and clamping her thumb between the patent pink lacquered fingers of his right hand. He then yanked the thumb sharply towards him. Miss Aberdeen screamed out in shock and pulled her hand from him. She made a fist and then stretched out her thumb and fingers from her palm. The pain had gone and the joint had re-located. Miss Aberdeen smiled nervously and the Owl Ladies went wild, even Carol, clapping and cheering. Alan leant back on his heels and, holding his cigarette between his teeth, joined in the applause too.

Later, Miss Aberdeen was drafted into the kids' side for our football match against the parents and teachers because we'd been a player short. During the game Dad gave away a free kick when he picked her up to move her out of his way. She'd been the only player between him and the goal. The Owl Ladies cheered again and Mum made Alan light another cigarette.

It had never really crossed my mind to be embarrassed that my Dad was dressed as an elderly woman, so I wasn't. I was probably as serious about football as Mum was about Guiding and macramé. Every game was important no matter what the opposition was wearing. I *had* once been mildly spooked during a fixture against Thornhill Juniors when their central defenders and right winger were wearing adult sized boots loaned to them by their teachers. This had given them a distressingly clown-like appearance. Despite this I'd managed to put my coulrophobia to the back of my mind for long enough to score a couple of late goals and seal a victory. The following Monday, the headmaster called me twinkle toes when he read out the match report in assembly and my nickname has been Twinkle ever since – more latterly, it's just Twinks.

Most people were serious in those days. Seriousness was very much encouraged. My sister and her friends were encouraged to be serious about performing Broadway musicals in strong regional accents for elderly people who were serious about wearing their coats indoors to watch them in draughty church halls. My sister was also serious about country dancing in the rain while wearing a black velvet waistcoat and leg-of-mutton shirt sleeves with some ribbons attached. By contrast, Dad was rarely serious. The closest he ever got was when he walked the three peaks late one autumn without a hat. He's never made any concessions to his baldness, he never wears hats and he's never had a bald man's hairstyle, just a normal one. He never shaves his head and he's never had a combover, he just has a normal hairstyle but with the bald bits missing. Back then, it was Robert Redford's hairstyle really but without the top bit. Sometimes if he'd not been to the barber's for a while he'd start to look like Terry Nutkins, the naturalist who had his fingers bitten off by Gavin Maxwell's otter. Two things you need to know about my dad; he's never worn hats and he's rarely serious about anything. Like I said though, back then everyone else *was* serious, my friends were serious about either football on wildly undulating pitches in the rain or marching down the high street playing brass instruments in the rain, a few were serious about both. Some other things to be serious about were: dressing in authentic period costume and re-enacting The War of the Roses on the moors in the rain, supercharging motorcycles and then racing them over a quarter mile next to the sewerage works in the rain, fell running in short shorts in the rain, becoming a drum majorette and proceeding down the high street by torchlight in a very short skirt and American tan tights while playing a xylophone in the rain, organising coffee mornings with people called Margaret, indoors, out of the rain.

Once, when we decided to set up a large tropical fish tank in the front room, Mum and Dad asked Alan to advise them because they knew Alan was serious about fishkeeping and home aquaria. Our two families had several days out together visiting the tropical fish stockists of the region with us kids in the boot of Alan's Volvo estate. Alan was genuinely knowledgeable on the subject having kept fish since boyhood. He was an expert on cichlids and proud of his breeding program. He had some big, graceful angel fish that Dad and I had both admired but Alan advised us not to start out with these. He told us they are deceptively quiet but can be aggressive and territorial if you don't know what you're doing. In the end we settled on a relatively low maintenance combination of platys, mollies, guppies and tetras and hadn't had to call on Alan's expertise again. As a result, we'd not seen much of him since.

****

Several years after the parents/teachers versus kids sports evening there was a knock at the door of Meadow View. Dad got up from the pretend marble breakfast bar where he'd been snacking on a slice of frozen Black Forest gateau. It was Alan. Dad invited him in and Alan explained that he was now the player/coach of a local Sunday League football team who were short of players for the upcoming season. He remembered Dad's close control and accurate crosses against the kids all those years earlier and wondered whether he would fancy signing on.

Dad briefly weighed up this chance to combat the early signs of a middle-aged spread he was forced to confront every morning in the floor-to-ceiling mirrors of his bedroom and then refused. It sounded far too serious. Instead, he suggested that I, now seventeen and still quite serious, might help out.

And so it was that I made my way to the Bare Knuckle Boys Inn where Alan's team met before and after games. It was a Sunday lunchtime, and it was busy. A man in his early twenties, covered in brick dust and homemade tattoos was playing a noisy bandit in the corner by the bar. His pasty friend looked on from under a woolly hat while sipping a pint of lager. He pulled hard on the cigarette which he held between his forefinger, middle finger and thumb in the pub style; lit end facing into the palm to avoid brushing it against people in crowded spaces. Another group of men was scattered around the pool table surrounded by pint glasses, kit bags and extra-long spirit levels. They chatted noisily amongst themselves. One of them, in his late twenties with spiky highlighted hair, a dusty builder's tan and a pair of nine carat hoop earrings jumped to his feet when the first salvo of gated reverb from Donna Summer's *Dinner with Gershwin* exploded from the juke box. He moonwalked the length of the pool table, neatly flipped a cigarette into his mouth and then popped some moves through the intro before hitting the vocal with a perfect falsetto. At this point one of the seated men who was trying to watch the pool match called him a fucking pouf and kicked him in the thigh with the sole of his trainer.

I glanced over to the bar and saw Alan perched on a stool on his own, he was sipping a bitter shandy and winding up his watch. I went over to join him, and we discussed tropical fish.

I got a lift to the game in Alan's new Volvo with four of the pool playing builders. During a group conversation comparing their police cell and prison-based experiences, the short and unnervingly aggressive team captain, Rod, asked me whether I'd ever been to prison. I said I hadn't. I'd never committed a crime of any sort as far as I could remember. I recalled the time when I was about twelve and had been into a shop with my friend Graham. Graham had stolen a roll of sellotape. For a moment I considered describing this event, claiming the misdemeanour as my own in an attempt to bond with my new teammates, but I thought better of it and the conversation moved quickly along to the subject of sex. Rod asked me whether I'd ever had sex with a married woman. I said I hadn't. I'd only ever even kissed two girls in my life and neither of them had been married. I didn't mention this either. Rod said he couldn't recommend sex with a married woman enough and that everyone should try it.

I played well. I won a penalty when I was brought down in the box, I set up a goal for the Donna Summer centre forward and I even scored myself when I got on the end of a diagonal through ball from little alpha male Rod. I was also one of only three players on the team not to have been booked. We lost 9-3.

At the Bare Knuckle Boys Inn after the game we were fed hot beef sandwiches, gravy and chips by a fat man in a pinny and black plastic rimmed glasses. My new teammates taunted him, calling him Raymond in a crudely offensive voice until he lashed out with his ladle and they all collapsed on the threadbare banquette seating in hysterical laughter. I made my excuses and went home.

When I arrived, Dad was in the garage getting some Asda vegetable cutlets out of the freezer. Nobody in the family was vegetarian and they didn't taste of anything much; Dad bought them out of convenience and habit, he's not really serious about food either. Mum came out of the front door. She was on her way to the divisional AGM with the Owl Ladies. Dad gave her a kiss and admired her bottom aloud in the style of Frankie Howerd as she walked over the road to Carol's VW Passat.

Dad and I drizzled our vegetable cutlets with a packet mix of own brand Au Poivre Sauce which we followed up with partially thawed Eccles cakes. We read scraps of the local paper at the pretend marble breakfast bar and I resolved to find something less serious than football to do with my time.

Transcendence 1999

Thursday 18th March 1999, 4.30am: The young presenter with the asymmetrical fringe smooths the black knee-length skirt under her thigh and sits down self-consciously in a high back swivel chair. She crosses her legs and turns to her guest, a man in his fifties whose complexion, despite the visible efforts of the make-up department, betrays an intense relationship with alcohol.

"I suppose first impressions are important," she prompts, twirling a pen between her fingers.

The man leans forward, his trousers are short enough to reveal an inch and a half of flesh above his navy blue socks. He recites his advice.

"The first impression is the most important impression you'll ever make." He clasps his hands between his knees and crosses his ankles under his chair. "Don't dress casually ... Don't wear trainers ... Don't wear too much jewellery ... Don't arrive late ... Don't chew gum ... Don't drink from a can... Don't have a moustache ... and above all, be positive." He leans back and smiles.

The presenter takes her cue and introduces a list of local job vacancies to the screen. They scroll along sans serif below her double-breasted cerise pink woollen jacket with oversized buttons:

....Commis Waiter Thirsk (£9,500p/a and meals on duty)....
....Deputy Manager Huddersfield Style Bar £16,000 plus bonus....

....Recruitment Sales Leeds (ambitious individual/desire to succeed)....

....Welder Fabricator Doncaster (time served/City & Guilds qualification/repairs to aluminium moulds)....

....Production Operative/Machine Operator Leeds Area (£5.00p/h near Harrogate)....

....Data Entry Clark Lincoln (Industry Leader/good computer skills)....

....Service Engineer Leeds (company car/laptop/travel to Italy)....

I sit on the edge of the slippery plastic sofa and drink my tea from the chipped Cadbury's mug I got with an Easter egg in 1984. The jobs scroll by and I look down at the spray of tiny hot rock holes in my shirt, the ink stain on the pocket, the split in the side seam of my trousers. I finish my tea, wrestle my feet into my shoes and tie what's left of the laces. I pull on my coat and pouch and turn off the TV at the set. "Don't forget you can send for our Yorkshire Jobseeker Information Pack by writing to this addr..." Phhtt.

Outside in the sodium orange drizzle, I coax the front door shut as quietly as I can. It hasn't closed properly since a neighbour smashed his way through it with a big stone from the garden wall; all he took was the carbon monoxide detector. I roll myself a cigarette and walk to the end of the street. Out on the main road, it's quiet. Apart from two untidy figures up ahead and the occasional car hissing past, there's no one else around.

Ahead of me, the two figures bustle along the pavement, the shorter one intermittently breaking into a jog to keep pace with the taller one. I lengthen my stride and as I gain ground, I make out a man and a woman, both very thin, with long hair and full-length anoraks. They twitch down the street, each with a large kit bag over their shoulder. I finish rolling my cigarette and crank my lighter. The noise prompts them to break into a run. Without turning to look back, they flee across the road.

I walk on, past the old methodist chapel which is now a carpet remnant centre and the old primary school which is now a mosque. I flick my cigarette end into a puddle and push my hands into my pockets. A man appears on the other side of the road outside the building that used to be a pub but is now nothing.

"You fucking traitor! You're fucking pimping yourself!" There's nobody else around. I glance over. The man begins shadowing me down the opposite side of the road. "You fucking whore! Think about it!" he yells, tapping his temple with his forefinger. He's in his late twenties, shaved head, tracksuit. I don't respond. He's still shouting. He says he's proud to have been up all night smoking weed instead of prostituting himself like me. "Fight me!" He yells. I glance up briefly but carry on walking in silence until he eventually gives up. "Agh, you silly cunt," he says as he disappears behind the old textile mending shed which is now a discounted pine furniture warehouse: *WE SELL BEDS!!!*

My footsteps echo under the viaduct as I slope down the hill and round the sweeping bend where the road runs parallel to what used to be a canal but is now a long narrow lake of stagnant water and litter. On, past the parade of takeaways and the leggy buddleias that sprout from the joints of the big canal-side wall.

I pass the church that's still a church and join the dual carriageway where I startle a fox, it bolts into the undergrowth outside the empty car park of the big Wickes. I climb the slip road, cross six lanes of almost deserted ring road, swing myself over the metal crash barriers and wander down through the town centre.

Brightly lit from above, a twenty-meter-long queue of women in their thirties and forties snakes across the pedestrianised precinct outside Next: *ALL SALE ITEMS HALF PRICE OR LESS.* CCTV cameras twitch in the fug of a hundred short haul perfumes. I 'scuse me' through the line and head down to the post office, converging with colleagues at every junction until I arrive at the yard in a group of ten or so.

Policing the entrance are three men in long Umbro football manager's coats. They chew gum vehemently, mouths open: the in-house Investigations Bureau. They present shiny badges in leatherette wallets to each approaching worker before searching their pouches for undelivered mail.

I skirt the shunting vans with drizzle in their headlight beams and climb the mid-century stairwell through a series of heavy wooden doors. The building is working: hustling and bustling, shouting, pushing, dragging, throwing, tipping. Postal workers pile letters into frames while their radios mash out a commercial playlist spew. Someone is singing songs from the shows in a hysterical falsetto. Someone is laughing loudly at loudly made observations about the shortcomings of other loud colleagues. I take my place at my frame.

"Morning," says Charlie, my next frame neighbour.

"Much on?" I ask.

"Yeah."

Charlie and I throw-off steadily while making plans for our retirement. We want to establish an exclusive dining club with leather button-back chairs and brandy served in silver rimmed balloons. Behind us, Pete and Nutmeg are discussing how best to remove the big cannabis leaf decal from the tinted rear window of the Honda Civic they bought at the auctions last night. Occasionally our new young university dropout boss,

Jason pokes his head around my frame and shouts above the noise.

"Less talking, more sorting!"

Charlie says he's noticed that whatever colour shirt the delivery office manager wears one day, Jason will be wearing the next.

Charlie, Pete, Nutmeg and I are the last out of the office. We fill a roll container with our stuff and wheel it to the lift. Charlie's ten year-old white Ford Scorpio is waiting, pristine inside and out apart from a tiny bubble of rust above the near-side rear wheel arch which has been disguised discreetly with a small flag of St George sticker. Charlie closely supervises the loading of the boot and then he and Pete climb into in the front, Nutmeg and I in the back. Charlie slips a cassette into the stereo, but Pete talks so loudly that he ejects it again almost immediately. Pete is keen to tell us about the beautiful Haitian princess/glamour model he's been writing to. She's been unfortunate enough to land herself in prison in Florida on some trumped up charges and needs financial assistance to pay for a decent lawyer.

"I got in touch through an advertisement I came across in a specialist magazine," explains Pete. "She sent me a picture of herself. I'll bring it in to show you. Dave Bell reckons it won't really be her, he thinks it might be some kind of scam. I'll bring it in. See what you think."

Charlie drops me off outside the Islamia Girls' School, the first drop on my delivery. It's still raining but not too heavily. I pull out the first bundle of mail from my pouch and set off up the steep terrace of back-to-backs. The streets are unusually busy because the council has organised a collection of bulky refuse for the afternoon. There are dozens of women in salwar kameez and sandals milling about with torn mattresses, old furniture and rubble sacks full of brick hardcore. I pick my way through the detritus on the pavements, through the ginnels and gates.

At the top of the terrace, I head down the other side of the hill delivering very little to the rows of council bungalows with plastic flowers and net curtains in the windows. There are few people on the streets around here. An elderly woman sits under her eaves in a wheelchair looking out across her council-clipped lawn to the cherry tree that's starting to bloom in the grounds of the day care centre over the road.

The flats and maisonettes at the bottom of the hill are quiet too. At the first block the concierge calls me over to tell me someone has smashed up the intercom system in the night.

"I'll watch you round on the CCTV and let you in to each block as you get there."

The flats smell. At the bottom of the stairwell in one block I narrowly miss stepping in a suspiciously human looking turd. In another, the entire end wall of the lobby has been smeared with streaks of blood into which obscenities have been scrawled. I leave a parcel in the housing of an electricity meter next to a stash of hypodermic needles.

The door to one of the flats has been attacked, someone has written *Cunt* on it in black marker and tried to set it alight. Its UPVC fascia has bubbled and split in the heat and the yellow foam interior has expanded and distorted. I knock with a registered letter and an anxious looking man answers. He thanks me and closes the door.

By the time I leave the flats and cross the main road, the sky has cleared and the streets are drying in the sun. At the junction of the new Gleneagles Way estate where the road leads down to the municipal golf course, I stop at the pouch box that has been defaced by D-MON K!D, $L!T K!D and EV!L BO¥. I unlock it and take out the bundles of mail, arranging all but one of them into my pouch. I fold my coat into the box, lock it, pull the elastic bands from the first bundle and head down the steep wooded cul-de-sac of detached and semi-detached fake sandstone fronted houses. Several times I have to leave my pouch at the end of a drive to avoid damaging any paintwork as I squeeze between the Mondeos and the pre-planted low-maintenance gardens. Plastic nursery tags flutter from immature birch and willow while the old beech canopy that surrounds the estate sways gently above them.

Deeper into the estate, the noise of the traffic gives way to the chatter of birds, the wind in the trees and the creaking of UPVC soffits and fascias as they warm in the sun. I knock at a house where a neat row of crocuses stand sentry in a small plastic wooden trough by the front door. A woman in her sixties answers wearing a navy blue housecoat. A shiny black Scottish terrier she calls Henry wags his tail and yelps around her ankles.

"Hold on a second would you, love?" she says as she grabs Henry by the collar, slides him across the plastic carpet protector to the front room where she shuts him in and he begins to bark. "Now then, love." I hand her a barcode to sign against. She scribbles a signature and scrupulously fills in the time, checking it on the brass rimmed wall clock in the hallway. "It's coming nice again now," she says. She asks me to pass her the two bottles of green top under the short length of 2x1 on the step. "It's to stop the blue tits getting at them. He always does that, he's ever so good. Thanks, love," she says as she backs inside the house and closes the door.

A couple of doors down a young man in his early twenties has reversed his red Fiesta Si onto the road for a clean. When I pass, he glances up from dressing his tyres,

"Y'alright, mate? You got owt for us? I'll save your legs."

I hand over his mail and carry on to the last few houses of the estate, two of which are still under construction. As I'm filling in a Sorry You Were Out card on the front step of an unoccupied house, one of the builders comes over and offers to sell me some cheap Viagra. I decline.

"Let all your mates know I can get it, won't you. I've been meaning to ask a postman for ages. I reckon the post office would be a right lucrative market."

The builder walks back to his truck smirking at the man in the passenger seat who grins back incredulously from under his highlighted 1980s style fringe. He's eating a sandwich from a white paper bag with the price tallied up on it in biro. He takes a big bite and laughs wildly, throwing his head back as the Viagra builder turns his baseball cap round the right way and gets into the driver's seat. The Viagra builder slams the door shut and says something to the 1980s builder who laughs again, spraying bits of his sandwich onto the dashboard; he pulls the cuff of his fleece over his hand and cleans off the mess. The two men speed away in the truck, laughing and waving to me from the window.

At the next house I fumble around for the latch among the gold fleur-de-lis tips of the new gate. After a moment I realise the gate is electronically controlled and there is no latch. I look around for a mail box but there isn't one so I try to attract the attention of the man on the telephone in the front room. Eventually I catch his eye and a couple of seconds later the gates begin to creep open. I edge past the car under the protective cover and the man comes to the door, still speaking into a cordless phone.

"She told me she was going to liaise with Jez this morning … Well, what can we do until she's spoken to Jeremy?" I hand over the barcodes and point to where I need a signature. "No, no, no, mate, we can't. It's not our problem." The man crouches on his haunches so he can rest the paperwork on his knee and sign with one hand. I give him half a bundle of mail. "I'll see what I can do. Everything's still in boxes here though. Look mate, can you get hold of Jez?" The man rolls his eyes at me, waves the bundle of mail, mouths his thanks and disappears back inside.

I make my way back to the pouch box and pack another bag before I set off down the main road towards town. It's busy now and the traffic crawls past me. I wave to a colleague who is delivering on the other side of the road and a man in a Vauxhall Vectra with a notepad fastened to his dashboard stops to ask for directions to Microworld. As I cut through the little park, a man with bad teeth and very white trainers asks me for a light for his cigarette.

My last pouch starts and finishes at Transcendence, the old textile mill by the canal on the edge of town that is now *A development of beautiful loft-style apartments in a peaceful waterside location.* The carpark is populated by exclusively German built cars: Porsches, BMWs, Mercedes and Audis. Inside, at the Coffee Mill café and reception area the Faithless song *God Is a DJ (Yes He Is)* is playing discreetly from invisible speakers. Cleaners in navy blue tabards with green binding and Marlboro Light shaped pockets sweep the minimal white interior with wide brooms, skirting the wire mesh baskets that house displays of pebbles and willow twigs. Kianna, the twenty-year-old receptionist, peers into a laptop. She has flawless skin and a big blonde wood desk with an inlaid brushed steel detail of the Transcendence monogram on the front. She looks up when she sees me approach with the mail. She tugs at the hem of her navy blue suit jacket and flicks her hair from her face. I hand her a bundle of mail and she asks me to wait while she goes through it. Out of the bundle of thirty or so letters she keeps seven and hands the rest back.

"These are nothing to do with us."

I put them back in my pouch to kill off later.

I leave The Coffee Mill and make my way round to the first block of the Transcendence complex. I press the Trade button on the intercom but I get no reply. I press it again and lean on the door. It doesn't move. I press a button marked Warden on the keypad. There's a fumbling crackle and then, "Hello?" I lean into the microphone and explain that I need to get into the flats to deliver the mail.

"Sorry, love," says the voice. "There's nothing I can do, I'm in a call centre in Bolton."

I buzz every flat in the block until somebody answers and lets me in. I repeat this operation at all five blocks until I finish my delivery and I walk the mile or so back to the office.

As I make my way through the gates to the now deserted delivery office yard, the doors of the lift open and university dropout Jason steps out in a pale lavender shirt open at the neck with an easy-care jacket thrown casually over his shoulder. He points a small remote-control device into the yard and the boot of a brand new BMW pops smoothly open. Nicky, the new cleaner, watches while she leans on the railings smoking a cigarette, her broom and dustpan propped beside her.

"You loved that, didn't you?" Jason tells her. Nicky smiles politely. I try to catch her eye over Jason's shoulder but she just looks at him and keeps smiling.

Charisma Club

January

The snow drifts on a mean northwesterly and the pulmonary silhouettes of the bare trees are disappearing in the noise. The GIVE WAY sign is fading fast but the mole catcher's laminated phone number is protected in its lee.

The river is high, swelling to only a couple of feet below the height of the old brick wall that contains it. A chair from the club floats by, snagging briefly in the overhanging branches of a tree before the current rushes it on.

Daz is tense at the wheel of the black Astra. He's in a hurry to get back over the tops. He's been to Manchester to spend his Christmas money on a pair of jeans and a small 'BEWARE OF THE WIFE' plaque to attach to his garden gate. He's not even married. The snow is four inches deep as he passes the sign for the summit of the M62, wipers thrashing against the blizzard.

At last, the Astra creeps into the carpark of the Charisma Club, headlights illuminating fly posters and chipboard. Daz gets out of the car and walks over to the one functioning window through which he sees a man lying motionless on a kitchen table.

February

The snow has all but thawed in the mucky meltwater carpark of the club. Daz's black Astra is parked-up next to the life-sized gorilla which stands hunched on an approximately circular plastic lawn next to a small group of plastic rabbits. The lawn is weighed down around its wonky perimeter with brightly painted rocks: red, blue, yellow, white. This tableau was designed and created by Stewart as the centrepiece of an ongoing makeover, a push to update the struggling club's image and bring in a younger crowd. It was the exertion of heaving the rocks into place before the weather swept the whole assemblage into the river that had resulted in Stewart falling asleep on the table the last time he saw Daz at the club.

It's been almost a month since Daz disappeared. A couple of days after he failed to turn up for work, Stewart called round to the house on Enoch Lane to try to rouse him. He discovered a note in Daz's handwriting Blu-Tacked to the front door.

GONE AWAY FOR A FEW ~~YEARS~~ DAYS Pleas put mail under shed door! Thanks!

Last Thursday, a photograph of Daz standing under the whale bone arch at Whitby briefly appeared on his Facebook page but apart from that nobody has heard from him.

March

It's a dank mizzling afternoon; overcast and low. Strip light floods from Just Eat windows onto the wet, chewing gum flags of the red, amber, green chili sauce pavements. Yvonne pulls up the hood of her puffa against the rain and muffles the idling bus, the fragments of conversations, the screeching tail-lift and all the mithering pigeons. Yvonne is in town with her big handbags. She ducks down the ginnel next to the boarded up Chinese Buffet and avoids the chugger with the upturned collars outside the Carphone Warehouse. She shoulders open the door of Hair Retreat. She needs to book a facial for Monday.

Later, Yvonne gets off the bus on Enoch Lane where she casts a brief glance through Daz's front window. She's almost given up wondering. She turns up the ginnel to the back of the terrace and takes the slippery back lane to her own house, past the half pigeon the sparrowhawk left on Thursday. She notices that the neighbour who wears flip-flops in the winter has tried to dispose of the big pile of rubbish in his yard by setting it alight, but it hasn't really worked; it smells and his wheelie bin has melted.

April

Despite, or perhaps because of Stewart's best efforts, the fortunes of the club have not improved. The SpongeBob themed Merry-Go-Round drew in a few extra customers for a week or two but once the novelty had worn off Stewart struggled to come up with the next innovation. He's missing Daz's input, Stewart has always felt that Daz has a good feel for this sort of thing.

In Enoch Lane, Yvonne is leaving her house. She leans heavily on the door and expertly coaxes the lock into place. She sets off up the path in a fug of something heavy by Yves St Laurent before pausing briefly to retrieve a leopard print bra from the damp grass below the washing line. She click-clacks back to the door in her heels and shoves the bra through the letterbox. Out on the back lane, dandelions and buttercups have colonised the path between the patchy asphalt. Yvonne glances up at the flip-flop neighbour's garden. The pile of partially incinerated rubbish is still there, as are the now skeletal remains of the pigeon in the middle of the lane. Out front, Julie is waiting in her big old Transit: Powered by Fairy Dust, Driven by the Devil, I'm not drunk I'm just avoiding potholes! It's filthy and so is Julie according to the graffiti written in the muck across the back doors. Yvonne clambers up into the passenger seat and endeavours to be as inconspicuous as she can in her efforts to avoid soiling her suit on the former contents of the overflowing ashtray. She brushes tab ends from the seat with a steadfast nonchalance. She's grateful for the lift.

Julie pulls up in the big new carpark of black Audis at G&D Valves: Passionate About Valves. Yvonne climbs down from the cab. She thanks Julie very much and shuts the door at the third attempt.

"Good luck, love," mouths Julie with a big thumbs up. Then she holds up an imaginary phone to her ear with her right hand, points to Yvonne with her left, and mouths "When you're done," before driving away. Yvonne tugs at the hem of her skirt, smoothes over the navy polyester/viscose blend and presses the intercom button firmly.

A man in overalls leads Yvonne through to a grey glass office where Helen Manager sits happily behind an open laptop. Helen is in her late thirties, slightly chubbier and shorter than average with a severe bob, satin lapels, expansive décolletage and a big smiley smile.

"Hi Yvonne, have a seat," she says with her head on one side.

Yvonne turns a clean and minimal high-backed chair towards her and sits down opposite Helen. Helen briefly outlines a short history of G&D and explains what they're all about:

"We're proud of our practical knowledge. We know what makes a successful application because we know how important it is for our customers to get what they need without having to interrupt their everyday operations," Helen is good at this stuff. She's confident and relaxed, "I want to foster this kind of attitude in the admin team too; efficient and customer focused," she explains. "Have you used Microsoft Office?" Helen is easy to talk to and Yvonne gives a good account of herself. At the end of the interview Helen Manager asks Yvonne whether she has any questions.

"Could I possibly use the toilet?" Asks Yvonne.

Helen smiles a big smiley smile, "Course you can. Go for it!" she beams.

May

Yvonne has been at the new restaurant in town with Helen Manager, the one everyone's talking about, the one with the reclaimed furniture and the music you'd forgotten you liked. She ate a chicken Caesar salad quite self-consciously. Helen went for the butternut squash and halloumi tray bake. They shared some white wine from New Zealand. It was nice.

Stewart's old Seat Leon has failed its MOT, so he decides to walk into town. He makes the most of the situation by stuffing a couple of bottles of Stella from the bar into his jacket pocket - the one without the hole. Outside, the streets are lined with sticky green tree litter and empty plastic bottles. It's been unseasonably warm. He passes the pebbledash semis with their St George crosses before turning down the student terrace of wheelie bins and marker-pen door numbers. At the bottom, on the corner, where the big old Mercedes with the Lithuanian plates has been abandoned, he bends to inspect a discarded cigarette packet. It's empty. He cuts through to the canal and opens a bottle of beer with a keyring opener as he makes his way on through the big patch of mother-die and wild garlic. On, past the discarded shoes, and the derelict ice cream van with the algae verdigris and perished tyres: *Make Every Day A Sundae*. As he circumnavigates the development of 'Desirable Loft Style Apartments in a Peaceful Waterside Location' Stewart notes the gravel rakes and Buddhas of the young professionals and considers some modifications to his gorilla diorama. He climbs the stone steps back out onto the street by the old Suzuki

Vitara with the spaniel in the back. On the adjacent wall there's a crooked sign re-purposed from a section of UPVC fascia board: *PARK HERE DIE HERE.* On, past the tangle of VHS video tape flapping from a tree, past the new BMW, parked half on the overgrown lawn of one of the back-to-backs. Stewart discards the now empty Stella bottle under a bush next to a bus stop and heads up the hill towards the high street. There are people around now: older people with wide brimmed hats, handbags and terriers, the middle-aged in North Face and earrings, the young with their tracksuits and food in paper bags.

"Hi Stew," says Yvonne. She's at the cash machine with Helen Manager.

"Oh, hiya, love," says Stewart, distracted, "You heard owt?"

"No. You?"

"Nah."

"How are things?"

"Oh, you know. Just off in here to see what's what," Stewart nods in the direction of the bank and sneers.

"Oh well, all the best," says Yvonne holding up crossed fingers, "Good to see you."

"Aye, you too, love. Take care."

"Who was that?" asks Helen Manager.

"Daz's partner at the club," says Yvonne. And they look at each other with an awkward grimace.

June

The addition of a metre tall statue of the Buddha into the gorilla diorama in the carpark of the club seems to have gone unnoticed as, unfortunately did the Little Mix tribute act that Stewart booked a couple of weekends ago. Today, Stewart is outside sweeping up discarded laughing gas canisters and deflated balloons in the same jeans and jacket he's worn every day for the last fortnight. He's got a bottle of Stella on the go to take the edge off. Daz's Astra sits on soft tyres; its coat of algae striated with the desire paths of molluscs. Stewart gazes at the tatty edifice of the club; the faded PVC banner strung across a boarded window: Watch 2018 World Cup Football Here. He has a good feeling about the phone call he's expecting this afternoon; a representative of the reenactment society has enquired about using the club as a practice space during times of inclement weather.

Yvonne is rounding off a weekend away with some colleagues from G&D. Earlier they were full of admiration for the bed chambers of Shibden Hall and now, out in the countryside, they walk off the last of their mild hangovers. Up the hill away from the lake, past swathes of pink valerian and foxgloves, the group stop to take in the view out over the valley. Yvonne feels her phone vibrating in her pocket. It's Daz.

"Hello," she says cautiously. There's muffled panic on the other end of the line before it goes dead without a discernible word. And there's Daz, at the top of Yvonne's Recents list for the first time in five months.

"Thanks, idiot!"

July

Following the recent death of popular local club allrounder, Grzegorz Garbarczyk, Stewart hosts a special night in his honour at the club. Grzegorz was popular on the circuit and had regularly compered Stewart's Big Saturday Night's in the nineties and early noughties. As they'd been close, the local paper had asked Stewart for his thoughts on Grzegorz's passing.

"I knew Gee Gee since school, he was a good lad. I always called him Gee Gee because I couldn't pronounce his name," Stewart said, a bit carelessly in his mum's opinion,

"How long have you known him, and you've never been bothered to learn how to say his name. Stewart, honestly!"

The night is a big success, reuniting many from the club's heyday. Stewart relaxes into his old self and enjoys the fact that people are enjoying themselves. Yvonne is there too. The intervening twenty years fall away and she finds herself instinctively gathering up empty glasses and returning them to the bar. And then, to the delight of the old regulars, she puts in a twenty minute shift serving drinks so the overworked barman can slip out for a smoke. At midnight Stewart giddily proposes a toast, employing one of Gee Gee's catchphrases to attract the attention of the crowd,

"Right, she said with a grunt!"

Afterwards, the dance floor fills at the first strains of Gee Gee's signature walk on song, Paul Weller's Peacock Suit.

The evening is rounded off by Gee Gee's son, Jake, who performs a near perfect rendition of Viva La Vida with his Coldplay tribute act, Goldplay.

Stewart lets the staff go as soon as he's called time and spends the next six hours clearing up. Afterwards, he rolls an old curtain for a pillow and falls asleep on the kitchen table again.

****

It's 5pm when Stewart wakes and lowers himself to the floor. He fills the kettle and switches on the radio just as the Drivetime weather presenter effuses,

"I love the idea of the summer sky as a dramatic falsetto..."

"I wish I had the time to think about what things I love the idea of" Stewart thinks aloud. He wedges open a fire door with an extinguisher and stands outside for a tea and a smoke. It's a nice evening, the concrete flags are warm under his feet as he contemplates the cloud of midges dancing in the sun. He thinks about Daz again, if anyone at last night's do had known why and where he'd gone they weren't letting on. Stewart's reverie doesn't last long before he instinctively casts his eye around the carpark, on the lookout. He sets down his mug and wanders gingerly over to inspect the four big Lidl bags which have been dumped between Daz's stupid Astra and the gorilla display. Crouching, with his cigarette between his lips he inspects the contents: forty-eight meerkat garden statues, several of which incorporate solar powered LED lamps. Stewart unfolds the sheet of Goldplay headed A4 which has been gaffer taped to one of the bags.

"Thanks for all your efforts yesterday. Thought you might be able to make use of Dad's meerkat collection at the club, Jake." Stewart picks up the bags and carries them back to the kitchen, aiming a low kick at Daz's Astra as he goes.

At G&D, Helen Manager calls Yvonne into her grey glass office and offers her a permanent position. There's no need for formalities, instead they hug and a share a demi of Champagne in the plastic picnic flutes with the screw-in stems that Helen keeps in her desk drawer. Yvonne's promotion has never been in doubt, she and Helen have hit it off from the start. Helen would love to have offered Yvonne the job sooner but she had to observe protocol.

August

Yvonne is on holiday: past the Amusement Arcade with the *Fully Air Conditioned Friendly Staff,* past the pillar box with the scabby yellow lichen, past the grey haired man in his 60s with the dark sunglasses and the bags for life, past the elderly woman who is cycling along the promenade with a flat tyre, past the drunk young man without a shirt and too much backside on display for Yvonne's liking, past the gold plated Mercedes with the red wall tyres, past the woman who *hearts* cockatoos according to the sign on her mobility scooter, past

Donuts 4 £2.00, past Beth and Trevor and all the other horses on the *Victorian Merry-Go-Round.* Past crocosmia, echinacea, hydrangea... Yvonne, Helen Manager, Julie, and Chris from sales climb aboard the funicular railway and disembark at the cliff-side bar with the dramatic views of the coastline below.

"And what can I get you, ladies?" asks the man in the old fashioned cream suit and Panama hat.

Back at home Stewart is running late from town: past the elderly Sikh man with the unusual trainers, past the cat on the broken fence, past the overflowing wheelie bins and the broken vibration plate left out for the binmen, past the crumbling homage to Michelangelo; a fig-leafed pudgy limbed David with a 1970s footballer perm, past the stained carpet and broken office chair, past the abandoned house with the bramble garden and Haribo wrapper trees, past the dead woodpigeon face down in the clover, past the torn settee, past the maisonettes with the rusty satellite dishes, past the stagnant canal, past the cobwebs and shuttlecocks in the cracked window, past several frost damaged Buddhas, past the elbow crutch propped against the street sign: *No Exemptions for Disabled Badge Holders*, past the man with the grey mullet and the hand drawn portrait of Emerson, Lake & Palmer on the back of his denim cut-off, past the bike frame chained to the *No Tipping* sign, past the woman running for the bus, past the laminated signs cable tied to the railings of the flyover: *WHO YOU LEAVING BEHIND?? HONEST THIS ISNT THE END YOU GOT THIS* ♥ ... A gaggle of reenactors has already accumulated at the entrance when Stewart arrives at the club. He apologises and makes his way through the doublets and hosen to unlock the doors. He sweeps the bank of light switches with the back of his hand as he passes on his way to hastily set up the bar,

"And what can I get you, gents?"

September

The reenactors have begun to frequent the bar of the club whether or not they are practising but Stewart knows their custom is probably too little too late. Nevertheless, he enjoys their company and has done his best to make them feel welcome. He's even offered to help out at their next event.

The old Mercedes bus rattles to a halt next to the bins in the carpark at Beeston Castle. Its condition is no worse than would be expected for a vehicle of its size after twenty years of being bounced down narrow unmade roads in search of poorly signposted make-do battlefields. The bodywork is scuffed and dented but the distinctive Betts Bakery livery is still just about legible down each side panel. The doors hiss open with a judder and thirty or so men in sack cloth disembark. Finally, Stewart switches off the ignition and climbs out himself. One at a time he slides the keys around the large metal ring, briefly inspecting each before he lands on the one that looks the most likely fit for the luggage hold. After a brief tussle with the lock, he opens the hatch and the men gather around while their repro woollens and metalwork are distributed. It's the first time Stewart has driven a bus since the club's heyday and he's happy to help out. It's not as though he doesn't need the money.

The cracked asphalt of Enoch Lane is dotted with early leaf fall and Yvonne is moving house. Yvonne, Helen Manager, Julie and Julie's partner, Tony are busy carrying the furniture and boxes from the house to Julie's van. The neighbour in the flip-flops watches absentmindedly from his burnt-out garden with a joint in one hand and a can of Rheinbacher in the other. On a final sweep through the empty rooms, Yvonne finds the key to Daz's front door half hidden in the drift of dry pelargonium leaves on the kitchen windowsill. She rolls it between her thumb and forefinger. The sun is disappearing as Yvonne makes her way down the sodden back lane for the last time. Out on the road she catches Julie's eye as she waits in the van a few doors down from Daz's house. Yvonne holds up two fingers and mouths "Two minutes."

She sets off at a half run up Daz's couch grass path for a last look on the off chance. Only a torn corner of Daz's note remains fixed to the front door, flapping gently from a mucky strip of sellotape. Yvonne turns the key in the lock and instinctively reaches inside for the light switch. The house smells damp and heavy. It's cold and untidy. It always was. The rolled up jogging pants, an improvised draught excluder, are still there, wedged behind the front door with a pile of unopened mail. Yvonne steps over them and pushes past the heavy old woollen peacoat hanging in the hallway. The front room is as spartan as it ever was: an enormous television set, the two seater sofa that Yvonne had persuaded Daz to buy to replace the old green velour armchair he'd inherited from his grandmother, a fallen down X-Files poster, a smattering of books—including the obviously unread 1980s VW Golf Haynes Manual Yvonne had bought as a present. On the windowsill, the pot plants Yvonne had also bought are dead. She turns and walks out, locks the door and posts the key through the letter box.

After unloading the van, Yvonne and the others toast the new house with the bottle of Moët that Helen Manager has brought with her. The weather is still just about mild enough to sit outside and stare out over the field of alpacas to the lights of the terraces in the valley below.

October

A skein of geese honk their way over the club. In the car park, a pair of blue Puma trainers sit in a puddle in front of the big swirling drift of discarded packaging and leaves. Next to the fire door stands the fridge from the kitchen, its plug dangling from its flex in front of the open freezer compartment. Next to the fridge, half submerged in leaves, sit three heavy-duty bin liners, half a dozen empty Budweiser bottles and a dead rat. On the approximate circle of plastic lawn now stands a large rusted yellow *Cheap As Skips* skip full of rubble, smashed plaster board, forty-eight meerkats, the gorilla and the Buddha. And, next to the skip, is the light patch of asphalt where Daz's Astra stood until it was towed away a couple of days ago. Stewart's texts and messages to Daz about the car have, as is now usual, gone unanswered.

Stewart wakes on the floor of the medieval Mercedes bus. He'd been reasonably comfortable when he'd made himself a bed across the back seats the previous evening but he rolled off in the night and now he has a dead arm and a piece of pop corn stuck to the side of his face. He climbs back onto the seats, pulls over the duvet that Craig the archer donated to him, and lies there, scrolling through the contacts on his phone.

It's an unseasonably clear day. Yvonne leaves for work from her new house on the estate of square brick-built semis, halved into triangles of light and shade by the low sun as it traverses the pantile roofs. Reproduction leaded lights sparkle and the orderly rows of lawns, cotoneaster, laurel and cypress are damp with morning dew. Yvonne locks up and slips into the little white Audi A1, unboxes a pair of large sunglasses and sets off.

November

Below the circling flock of squabbling jackdaws the woods have turned red and yellow. An old Betts Bakery plastic bag is tangled in the lower branches of a beech and the hills in the distance are shrouded in mist. The graffiti by the river reads simply *CHILL* as Stewart poses under a rainbow with his new rescue

Border collie, Ian. Craig the archer takes their photograph for the reenactment society's Facebook page. It's been a difficult month on a diet of mainly Flame Grilled Steak McCoy's and cheap beer. Nights have been spent on friends' sofas or on the back seats of the bus, cold and sleepless. Stewart's luck changed a couple of weeks ago when some of the regulars from the club had a whip round and he secured a flat in town. Next week he's training to bring his driving qualifications up to date with a local coach operator.

Stewart, Craig and Ian the collie cut through over the bridge and emerge by the derelict youth club building at the bottom of Enoch Lane. From here Stewart can see the For Sale board outside Daz's. They divert to the top where Stewart peers in through the window of Daz's front room. The two-seater and the television have gone.

Helen Manager has, of course, organised a Helen Manager style bonfire evening. Yvonne, Julie and the two Chrises (sales and accounts) have been helping to prepare. There are baked potatoes, a big tray of parkin, discount Standard Fireworks (Julie's Tony works there) and Prosecco in the plastic flutes with the screw-in stems. The fire itself is located in the field at the back of Helen Manager's new build estate of detached repro-stone houses with repro bricked up window tax windows and prominently mounted burglar alarms. It's not a big fire but, as Helen points out, it's enough to counter the uncomfortably chilly breeze and steady rain,

" … And that's the main thing, isn't it?" she says with a smiley smile.

December

It's raining steadily as Stewart pulls the medieval Mercedes up to the kerb between Sarah's Wallpaper & Paint and the Jamia

Masjid Abu-Bakr. An orderly queue of men in sackcloth, North Face, Santa hats and antlers make their way aboard. Today is the Medieval Reenactment Society Christmas Do and it's Stewart's first day out as a fully qualified driver. This thirty-year-old tradition involves a muddy skirmish in the foothills of the Peak District followed by pizza and beer back at The Ship Inn, a 1960s brick built pub on the ring road opposite the big Betts Bakery. As the bus climbs towards the moors, the weather worsens and by the time Stewart opens the doors, the combatants are almost swept from the bus by a gale. The men form a scrummage around the luggage hold before they re-emerge, helmeted and clutching swords and poleaxes. They straggle through a gate and pick their way around miry puddles to an adjacent field where, after a short huddle, they re-enact the War of the Roses for three quarters of an hour. Somewhere above them on the moor, a clay pigeon shoot is underway, the pop, pop of the guns swirls around them in the squall.

Yvonne is looking down on a busy Canary coastline, the green ocean dotted white with cresting waves, yachts, probably dolphins and god knows what else. The island is terracotta and turquoise, volcanic cactus scrub criss-crossed with dust roads, flared at the edges with sea foam. There are white patches of geometric villas in an irrigated oasis of palm trees and cars. For her safety and comfort she remains seated until the plane has stopped and the captain has switched off the seatbelt sign. After that, she's away.

Jonnie Rabbett's Shooting Club

Jonnie Rabbett has a wind-blown complexion and an off-kilter centre of balance. He wears green things and he lives on a hill. He is in charge. He drives an old Suzuki Vitara with a spaniel in the back and it was his idea to write the name of the club in Tippex on the ear-defenders when they started to "Go Walkies." Jonnie doesn't speak much, but when he does, he shouts because of the howling gales and because everyone is wearing ear defenders.

Again, in the half-light, Ben and Kieran are walking into the weather through the mucky slews of fallen leaves. They climb steadily towards Jonnie Rabbett's hill farm in silence; they gave up talking about half an hour ago when they could no longer hear each other above the scattershot sleet and the wind thrashing about in the trees. Heads down, hoods up, they watch the run-off stream under their boots, carrying away beech nuts and twigs behind them.

At the top of the hill, the boys vault the drystone wall in the usual place and cross the couch grass carpark at the back of the clubhouse - the small wooden chalet that has somehow clung to this exposed valley side for over forty years. As they round the corner, Jonnie Rabbett appears at the door with Brown Hound, his careworn springer. He taps his waxed sleeve at the wrist and yells something about the time, but the boys can't hear him and he's forced to continue delegating through basic sign language and muffled shouts: the Down-the-Line range for Ben, the Springing Teal trap for Kieran. Jonnie Rabbett offers up the battered sack of bright yellow, thirty year old oilskins that are far too big for anyone. He has written the name of the club on each garment with an indelible marker even though nobody can remember any of them ever going walkies.

Kieran's trap is housed in a rusty oil tank which has been painted racing green many times over many years, its open end faces out from a ridge above the valley. Kieran clambers inside, his movement restricted by his enormous oilskins. An icy northwesterly throws down the rain as he wedges himself inside, one leg either side of the trap. At least he's out of the weather. Jonnie Rabbett appears and walls him in with clay pigeons, lining the tank three boxes high down either side. Kieran makes himself as comfortable as possible and then tears into one of the boxes, nicking the tip of his forefinger on a carton staple as he does so. He switches hands to stem the blood with his mouth and twists to tear at the box again, this time he rips out a strip of cardboard big enough to expose the stack of clay pigeons. He loads up the trap and waits. There isn't the room to sit up straight, so until the first shooters arrive, he hotches forward a couple of inches and cranes to peer out at the sodden fell.

After five minutes or so, Jonnie Rabbett is hammering on the side of the tank to signal that the first squad of shooters have taken their stands. Kieran shuffles into place with his back flat against the wall of the tank. He tilts his head to one side in the restricted space under the rusty steel roof. He blows the dew drop from his nose, fumbles around for his ear defenders and takes off his gloves with his teeth.
    A muffled "Pull!"

Kieran springs the trap, throwing a clay pigeon up about a hundred feet. There's a gunshot, but there's no time to look up, he has to reload. As he leans forward to slot the next clay pigeon into place, slivers of rust flake into his hair and face. He blows out gritty orange rainwater from his mouth; the same ferrous tang as the blood from his finger.

Kieran settles into a routine of hectic trap feeding followed by the quiet periods between squads when he stares out through the weather down into the valley until Jonnie Rabbett thumps the side of the tank again.

After a couple of hours, the rain all but stops while the wind never lets up. During a break, Kieran peers out of the tank and watches a small bus pull off the road down the valley. The doors shudder open and twenty or so sturdy looking men in sackcloth file out. They scrummage around the luggage hold for a bit and then re-emerge, each helmeted and clutching a ten-foot pike. They straggle through a gate and pick their way around miry puddles to an adjacent field where, after a short huddle they re-enact the War of the Roses for three quarters of an hour. Their attempts at authentic medieval cries fetch up on the wind and Kieran wonders if the reenactors are warm enough and whether they are completely out of range of the guns.

Jonnie Rabbett hammers on the tank and Kieran begins another round of activity. The trap springs, launching the clay pigeon almost vertically, Kieran hears the gun discharge but the clay remains intact. It hovers momentarily at the peak of its trajectory before the wind catches it and hurls it back the way it came ... The arm of the trap cocks again and Kieran stares at it, confused. He doesn't load. The trap springs again, empty. It cocks again ... Kieran becomes aware of a dull pain on his head above his right eye. He feels at it. It's warm. He brings his hand away, it's red with blood. He looks down. He's covered in blood. His yellow oilskins are streaked with rivulets of red. Jonnie Rabbett's head appears round the front of the tank.

"You all right, lad? Oh, bloody hell, you're not, are you?" He pulls Kieran from the tank and helps him over to the clubhouse to get cleaned up.

"What happened?" Jonnie asks.

"I think the wind swept one of the birds back in," says Kieran.

Inside the clubhouse, Barbara 'Bunny' Rabbett, Jonnie Rabbett's mother, looks up from the counter where she's pouring tea from an enormous, dented aluminium teapot.

"Come on, love," she says, and she lifts the hinged countertop. She fishes out a couple of mugs from the washing up water, soaks a paper towel in it and wipes at Kieran's head. "It's not so bad, love. It'll be right," she says as she bins the bloodied towel and slams a pork pie into the microwave in the same movement.

Kieran shuffles out from behind the counter carefully so as not to dislodge any breakables in his blood-stained oilskin fat suit, then he flumps down at the small round table below the *Wines of Spain* bunting. Bunny isn't far behind with a pork pie and a mug of instant coffee. She carries them over on the metal Perrier tray that features a colourful picture of a young woman wearing nothing but a wide-brimmed sun hat and bottle tops over her nipples. Kieran catches his reflection in the stainless steel lid of the sugar dispenser; his forehead is still smeared with blood and there's the starting of a black eye. Bunny adds a blob of brown sauce to the lid of his pie and a good measure of Scotch to his coffee.

As groups of bedraggled shooters begin filing back into the clubhouse, occluding the windows with their condensation, Kieran heads back out to the range. He crawls inside the tank again and stares out over the valley. The bus and the medieval soldiers have gone, there's a muddy patch in the field where the war had been most concentrated but other than that there's no way of knowing it had ever taken place.

Kieran spends another couple of hours flinging clay pigeons up in the air before Jonnie Rabbett pounds on the side of the tank for a final time to let him know the last of the shooters have left the stands.

"Well done, lad. How's your head?" He says, as he reaches out a hand to pull Kieran to his feet.

"It'll be right." Kieran stands up and stretches himself. His head is sore.

The rain returns as Ben and Kieran help to clear the ranges. They rake the stands for spent cartridges and shovel them into the bucket of the tractor, then Jonnie Rabbett hands over the key for Ben's trap hut.

"There's some empty boxes in there you can stack any clays that's not broken in. Lock us it up when you're done!" he shouts, then he waves his lanolin arms about roughly in the direction of the range.

"There'll be a right load of them down there!"

Jonnie climbs into the cab of the tractor with Brown Hound and they head off to pull thistles in the top field while the boys trudge up the steep slope to the breeze block hut. They take out a couple of cardboard boxes each and head back, the wind shoving them down the range at a run. They hurdle bilberry and heather to the gully at the bottom where they know most of the clays will have landed. Kieran starts in one corner and Ben in the other, rooting about on hands and knees under tussock and reed grass for serviceable birds. When they find them, they run their fingers around the rims to loosen any slugs and sheep shit. If the clays have landed upside down, they are full of ice which they dislodge with a gentle tap against a partly collapsed dry stone wall. When the clays are clean, they are stacked neatly in the now damp cardboard boxes. The work is fiddly so they can't wear gloves and their hands are scratched and numb with cold.

It takes about an hour for Kieran to fill his boxes, then, one at a time, he clambers back up to the hut with them, hugging them to protect them when he inevitably stumbles on the rough ground. He stacks them in the shelter of the hut and sits on his hands for a while to warm them. Staring out at the relentless gale, a thought occurs to him; he grabs a couple more boxes from the hut and climbs up onto the roof. Telegraph wires are straining at their poles the full length of the valley.

"Ben!" he yells.

The figure at the bottom of the range looks up.

"Catch!"

Kieran throws one of the boxes up as high as he can, the wind snaps at it and it flies the full length of the range to the gully where Ben leaps to his left and pulls it down. Kieran throws another box and the same thing happens. The boys work to perfect their technique, throwing and catching more boxes until all Kieran needs to do is hold the box above his head with his right hand while Ben stands with his arms outstretched down in the gully fifty yards away. Kieran releases his grip and seconds later the box hits Ben square in the chest whereupon he wraps his arms around it and sets it down, securing it with a stone from the collapsed wall. Eight more times Kieran lets a box go with exactly the same result. It's exhilarating. Every time a box hits Ben in the chest, the boys whoop with laughter. The strength and direction of the wind is unremitting. They swap positions, Ben comes up to the hut and Kieran goes down to the gully. Kieran catches the boxes in the same way. Over and over again they throw boxes and catch them. The wind never varies. Kieran says it's as though time has got stuck in a loop and Ben says it's fucking mad.

After a half hour of throwing and catching boxes, the boys stack the rest of the salvaged clay pigeons in the hut and lock it up behind them.

Back at the clubhouse, Kieran inspects his head in the mirror, the black eye doesn't seem any worse, but the area around his cut forehead is swollen and bruised.

"It'll be right," says Ben.

"It'll be right," says Jonnie Rabbett as he counts out the boys' wages in cash.

There's not a lot over £20 each once Bunny has deducted the price of coffee and pork pies, but they supplement their income on their way home by picking magic mushrooms to sell in the pub. They'll be back next week and again the week after that ... stuck in a loop.

Natural History

It was the morning after a particularly stormy night, the same night our neighbour torched his shed. I didn't know this neighbour very well, we worked different shifts so we rarely bumped into each other. He was recognisable though for his striking appearance: tall and thin with a long scar that ran from the top to the bottom of the left side of his face. Style wise, he favoured the hairdo and eyewear of Nick Knox of the Cramps combined with the threadbare knitwear and army issue boots of a badger baiting youth worker from the 1970s. He'd once sold me a car battery for a fiver. Anyway, that night's strong winds ensured his fire not only spread to next door's fence and wheelie bin but also badly scorched their new secondhand Austin Montego. It was specifically the damage to the Montego which prompted the noisy fist fight in the street below my bedroom window at 2am.

"Look at the state of my fucking car you stupid fucking twat!"

The fire was still smouldering as I walked past it at 7am. As on most mornings back then, I was on my way up to the moor at the end of Frederick Street to release another mouse from one of the humane traps into which I'd naively put so much faith and peanut butter. It was as I rounded the corner into William Street that I happened upon the small ziplock bag full of exotic looking feathers. A flash of green caught my eye amongst the wind tossed takeaway-styrene of another tangled litter trap. I crouched and reached out an arm between the rotten fencing and the last remaining asbestos panel of what was once one of those mid-century garages for an Austin 1100. At full stretch, holding on to a deformed hawthorn for balance, I managed to snag the bag between my index and middle fingers. I stuffed it into my pocket and continued on my way to the moor where I released the mouse as usual.

Back at home I turned the key in the nightlatch, shouldered open the door and watched as a dozen or so mice scattered across the kitchen floor for the cover of the battered skirting. I swept the table top for droppings and put the kettle on; I disinfected the table so often in the couple of years I lived in that house that by the time I left I'd worn away any trace of varnish. I reached for the vintage Ty-Phoo tea caddy from the high shelf and dropped a tea bag into a mug. I'd started storing all my mugs, bowls and pans upside down in the cupboards after I'd found droppings and sticky yellow piss stains in them. I also kept all my food in metal containers otherwise the mice would eat it before I did. I'd once found a mouse asleep in a double-boxed pack of Shreddies and from that point on I scoured the charity shops for all the old bread bins, biscuit tins and sweet jars I could lay my hands on. I sat at the table and drank my tea, making sure I coughed, sniffed and shuffled my chair regularly lest the mice got the impression I'd left the room and decided to reemerge. Remembering the bag of feathers, I pulled it out from the pocket of the jacket on the back of my chair and tipped out the contents onto the table: six complete and very beautiful iridescent hummingbird skins. Stunning greens, pinks, purples, yellows and blues. Labels attached to each specimen read *Property of Bradford Museums* in an old-fashioned typewriter typeface.

I laid out the skins in front of me while I finished my tea. I stroked and teased the feathers into place until they were neat and pristine. They were obviously old and very fragile but were in good condition. They were beautiful.

I'd thought about keeping the bird skins but a few days later I phoned directory enquiries for a contact number at the museum. Remarkably the person answering the phone knew immediately what I was talking about. She explained that on that stormy night, the night my neighbour set fire to his shed, she decided to take a box of bird skins home with her to try to identify them over the weekend. She said she had a hell of a commute. Her usual hour-long drive took her almost two and a half hours and had been a stressful experience. Twice she was diverted around fallen trees and at one point the car in front was hit by a child's trampoline.

"It just came out of nowhere!"

When she finally turned off the main road, the flames from the neighbour's shed fire were leaping over the wall and across the street.

"By that point I just didn't care, I just drove straight through it!" she said.

She eventually arrived at her home up by the moor at the end of Frederick Street but when she opened the boot of her car a squall had swept the box of bird skins out of her hands. She scrabbled around with a torch and located all but one bag of specimens.

And so it was that I set off again, past the scorched ground where the shed had been, to reunite the birds with the curator of Natural History who was impressed that I'd known they were hummingbirds. I left her to ponder the specifics and went back home to my mice.

An Inventory of the Family Rubbish

The following is an annotated transcript: brother and sister, Dominic and Natalie (along with Nat's partner, Rob) are home to visit their parents, Alison and Geoff. They are delving into a pile of family keepsakes that Alison collects and stores in an old suitcase labelled Family Rubbish.

Family Rubbish #1

A scuffed WHSmith's ring binder in black with a picture of Robert Smith from The Cure stuck to the front with aged and brittle sellotape. Inside, there are just two leaves of lined A4 paper, one of which is blank. The other bears the following handwritten text. No names. No dates.

> Grandad Lockwood told us how Paul Cézanne was the father of modern art because he ignored established rules about perspective, composition and bothering to make stuff look 'real'. When we all went to Paris to look at Cézanne's paintings, Grandad Lockwood told us about the solidity of the painted surface and the architectural style. He pointed out the wonky still life tables as evidence that Cézanne was interested in creating a more authentic composition.
>
> I understood it, but I didn't really get it.

I started to use Cézanne's style when I needed to represent something solid and authentic. I thought this made me an artist too but Grandad Lockwood said it didn't. He said Cézanne was *obsessed* with making his art and he couldn't give a shit about what anybody else thought. He said he was only doing it for himself and as far as *he* was concerned everyone else could just fuck off. Grandad Lockwood said it was this that made Cézanne a great artist. He said Cézanne's aim wasn't to create an effect or to illustrate a point or to deliberately turn his back on what had gone before. His famous quotes about apples, cones, cylinders, tree trunks, drawing in paint and whatnot were just him trying to explain his work to people who didn't understand it. Problems arise when his quotes and other peoples' quotes about him start to take the place of his art.

Dom: This is mine. I remember the folder but I don't remember writing that. I was such an arse!

Nat: You weren't an arse, you were just young. We were all arses at that age. Anyway, it makes a lot of sense. What's wrong with it?

Dom: Oh, you know... Do you remember the Paris trip with grandad?

Nat: Yes, course. It was ace. Grandad was ace.

Dom: Yeah! Completely mad.

Nat: In a good way.

Family Rubbish #2

A 3x2" black and white photograph of an Invacar 'invalid trike' parked on an unmade road at the end of a row of terraced houses.

Dom: That's his trike, Grandad's. No way! I've not seen that one before.

Alison: That's an old one. Mind you, he had that trike for years. Do you remember when they first built the M62 and he drove all the way to Cleethorpes on the hard shoulder? He was a silly old sod, honestly. Where's that photo of Iris and Ken's wedding where he's got his shoes on the wrong feet?"

Nat: Oh my God!

Everyone: *laughter*

Family Rubbish #3

Russell's last Silvine memo book (2012). Red with geometric doodles on the cover. Staples outlined in biro. Inside, the pages are densely filled with sketches and neat and legible handwriting. Some sections, such as the one that follows, have been written completely perpendicular to the guide lines on the page, the book having been turned on its side.

Nat reads aloud:

> You suspect commerce because it takes
> art hostage and makes it say things it

doesn't mean. You suspect politics for the
same reason.

You are suspicious of craftsmanship
and skill, you think the single-minded
discipline it necessitates precludes a
receptiveness to new ideas.

You suspect street art because you think
it says less about the world than it does
about the egos of its practitioners.

You suspect provincial art because
it consists mainly of half-arsed,
small-enough-to-post, lazily juxtaposed
de-contextualised found-objects that
offer at best the same level of insight as
a single sentence in a good novel but
are nevertheless afforded the 'respect' of
a whole white-washed wall in a pop-up
gallery on a derelict high street.

You are suspicious of the trends of
cosmopolitan art: fluorescent powder
paint, broken household appliances from
the 1980s, cardboard and hardboard,
white emulsion and duct tape, a bolt
of cloth with some writing on it. You
suspect these artists are not leading as
they claim (see first point: commercial
hostages).

You worry that the dilettanti have built
a career path all over what used to be
unspoiled art wilderness and that they,
with their rictus grins, and their apron

strings and their hairstyles and their knitting and their junk sculptures and their colour coordinated found objects and their cushions-with-stuffing-coming-out and their cling film nudes and their glass-from-a-skip and their director of public services/arms-dealer partners are on a never-ending self-regulating negative loop. And you worry that nobody can get anywhere near the boat anymore, let alone rock it.

And most of all you are suspicious of yourself. You are probably shit at art for a thousand reasons, most of which you can't even conceive of.

So you decide to drink some alcohol and smoke some cigarettes.

Geoff: Agh! Sad. Did you ever meet Russell, Rob?

Rob: Only once. Heard a fair bit about him though. Wasn't he a bit of a handful?

Geoff: He liked a drink.

Alison: He drank himself into oblivion. His liver was shot and he was only forty-five.

Geoff: He was a good bloke really, just never found his way.

Alison: I never found out what happened to Dawn. She was lovely. She left him in about, um, it would have been about 2005 because it was just before John and Cynthia's Ruby wedding. She never turned up and we didn't know why until afterwards. I didn't blame her. I know she really wanted kids. Do you remember that bedsit they had in Fearnley Road? It was disgusting, I don't know how people can live like that. Iris tried to track her down when he died but I don't think she ever found her."

Family Rubbish #4

A VHS cassette tape with *Boat Yard Jack Rowat film Gary June 1993* written on a sticker on the 'spine' in black marker pen.

Geoff: What the hell's this?

Alison: It'll be one of Gary's.

Geoff: Fucking oddball.

Alison: Geoff!

Geoff: Well!

Geoff gets up and starts fiddling with the elderly VCR and box-shaped television set.

Geoff: It works, look. Pass us it here.

Geoff slides the cassette into the machine and presses play.

The film is a clumsily spun eulogy to Jack Rowat, the now deceased doyen of model boat builders who had a small media career promoting his craft on children's television in the 1970s and 80s. It's obvious that filmmaker Gary is an enthusiastic apologist but no amount of spin can quite cover up the fact that Mr Rowat was a sinister, selfish and possibly violent sociopath.

The film is compiled in a workmanlike manner from three sources:

1. Gary's self-originated hand-held camcorder footage.
2. Clips from Mr Rowat's semi-professionally produced instructional/promotional videos.
3. Scratchy VCR recorded selections from the TV appearances Mr Rowat made during his 'heyday'.

In the camcorder sections of the film, Gary's heavy breathing and throaty acquiescent laughter is audible on the original soundtrack. The syntax of his overdubbed voiceover is stilted and articulated with the self-consciously precise diction that enthusiasts tend to favour:

> "Jack Rowat was born in 1928. He originated from Solihull and suffered a bitter childhood which resulted in him having no faith in people. He started out in the world of work as a joiner before becoming a salesman. But his great ambition was always his love for model boats. He began with gas powered boats in a lock-up in Bloxwich near Walsall and then eventually he moved into the buildings on the Worcester & Birmingham canal that became the Jack Rowat Model Boat Yard mentioned in the famous song by the group Frank Moran's Big Medicine Band.
>
> Jack was a fair man with the right person but anyone who annoyed him or disagreed with him or basically got his back up usually went home feeling rather miserable. To some people the name Jack Rowat brings a shudder, a vision of a man

who was difficult, strong minded, and
downright temperamental. But those who
met him and treated him with respect,
Jack would often reward with intriguing,
interesting information."

The above section of voiceover accompanies some handheld footage of Jack in wire rimmed glasses, a goatee beard and a Purdey bob, greying at the temples. He is in his meticulously planted Britain in Bloom style garden in front of an almost imperceptibly bay window with a reproduction cartwheel attached to the wall below it. In the driveway is a mustard yellow Triumph Toledo with a trailer onto which a half scale model of Sir Henry Segrave's Miss England has been loaded. Mr Rowat is inspecting his borders. He is visibly enjoying hunting for slugs with a blow torch.

Gary's voiceover goes on to suggest that Mr Rowat was in fact an inspirational figure on the fringes of progressive pop culture and not just a quirky footnote in the cultural history of the era—the more commonly held view among the few who have an opinion on him at all. The film cuts to footage of Frank Moran's Big Medicine Band performing on The Old Grey Whistle Test and a post Operation Yewtree interpretation of the lyrics gives them a more sinister feel than they had perhaps had hitherto:

> In Jack Rowat's model boat yard
>
> we always found it hard.
>
> Then one day we went to play
>
> and the law had taken Jack away.

Rob: Christ, is this for real?

Geoff: Told you he was an oddball.

Dom: What happened to Gary, is he still around?

Geoff: Pfft, no idea. I wouldn't go Googling him, God knows what you'd find.

Family Rubbish #5

Iris's letter from hospital. White envelope, handwritten in blue biro, first class stamp. Postmark, Huddersfield, 24th Feb 2014.

Alison reads aloud:

> Dear Alison,
>
> As you know I've not been well but my convalescence (and the morphine!) has afforded me the opportunity to consider my wellbeing more generally. I have decided that from now on I am going to be positive in my outlook and not get mired in all this adversarial us-and-them nonsense. To this end I've been considering whether there is anything at all that the peoples of the world, regardless of religion or culture, have in common. Is there anything that we can all unite behind? Well, I believe there is. Through the haze of a wide variety of painkillers, I think I've found something: Our tolerance, our indulgence even, of mollycoddled self-important wankers. For example, we have no quibble with our younger wankers in particular who love to draw attention to themselves by driving noisy fifteen-year-old hatchbacks up and down the town while shouting

lewd requests at our young women. Neither do we mind when our wankers aggressively proclaim their sporting affiliations in the high street in front of some toddlers on a Saturday lunchtime. All around the world we allow our wankers to wave their guns in the air, have their names engraved on shiny things, shake the hands of other wankers on the news. We let them own yachts, fast cars, newspapers, banks, governments, countries, the Royal Mail. We love it when one of our wankers wears flamboyant spectacles and interrupts an award ceremony because he didn't win, or when an ageing one of our wankers is photographed wearing an open-necked shirt and boot-cut trousers to grope a glamour model. The list is endless, which proves my point: All the peoples of the world can unite in peace and harmony through the shared love of wankers.

Love to the family,

Iris

PS Nat's lemon drizzle was fabulous

Alison: I bloody love Iris.

Everyone: *laughter*

Nat: How is she?

Alison: She's all right, all things considered. I spoke to her on Sunday. I asked her how her hip was but she was just going on about Dominic Raab; he's blocked her on Twitter.

Family Rubbish #6

Marco Pirroni's guitar pick/plectrum. 3x3x3cm equilateral triangle with rounded corners. Approx 1mm thick. Cream/white mother of pearl effect plastic with a slightly off-centre wolf's head motif printed on one side in black with an outline of yellow. Surface shows signs of wear.

Dom: Marco Pirroni gave me this. Marco Pirroni from Adam and the Ants? It was a job I did. It was for CBBC about the Electric Brae; that road in Scotland with the strange topography that makes it look like your going uphill when your actually going down. It was for a programme he was presenting, so he came with me. I drove all the way up to Ayrshire with him. He brought a cushion off his settee to sit on, on the passenger seat...

Rob: Eh?

Dom: I know, we were in the old Picasso. He lowered the seat as far as it'd go and then put the cushion on top, I don't know why. He was only wearing a pair of jeans and a t-shirt and I just remember thinking "He's gonna be freezing!" Anyway, when we got there, we set up all the gear and Marco did his thing; he did this interview with this local guy on an old Honda C70 step-through. And then, to demonstrate the optical illusion, he got on the pillion and they rode off up the hill together without even starting the engine.

Geoff: Haha, of course they did. Perfect...

Dom: I've just remembered! The other bloke was called Marco too, the local bloke on the scooter, I knew there was something, they were both called Marco. That's weird, isn't it?

Rob: Yes, coincidence.

Dom: I know! Anyway, he was great, Marco, Adam & the Ants Marco, and he said he'd really enjoyed it. He said he was hoping to do more of that sort of work which is funny because I've not seen him in anything else since."

Family Rubbish #7

A signed black and white photograph of Brian Wilde, Bill Owen and Peter Sallis AKA Foggy Dewhurst, Compo Simmonite and Norman Clegg of the long running BBC sitcom *Last of the Summer Wine*. The photograph is in good condition with only slight yellowing around the edges of the white border. Brian Wilde and Bill Owen's signatures have faded from the original black to a red/brown colour whereas Peter Sallis's, although faded slightly, is still clearly black.

Nat: Haha, brilliant! I can't believe you've still got this.

Rob: What is it?

Geoff: That's from when we lived in Holmfirth. All the kids got given one. It's a signed photograph of the cast of *Last of the Summer Wine*. It's actually signed, not printed.

Rob: Let's have a look.

Nat: We carried them around in little plastic wallets and they entitled us to discounts on past their sell-by-date Creme Eggs from Hobson's Choice and Ciderkin from the bar at the Phoenix (Youth Club).

Dom: God, yeah. Great days!

Nat: Just think, nowadays, kids in Holmfirth have to pay the same as everyone else for their unhealthy snacks because *Last of the Summer Wine* isn't on telly anymore.

Family Rubbish #8

Another of Russell's Silvine memo books. This one is from 2005 because it says so in 3D calligraphic biro on the cover. The following is from about two-thirds in. This time Russell's handwriting is not so precise but it approximately follows the guide lines on each page.

Dom has been flicking through the memo book and reads aloud the following:

> Despite having studied art for five years and having practised as an artist for a further fifteen, I have never called myself an artist. There are three reasons for this:
>
> 1. Because I couldn't be more serious about art. I revere good artists. Whenever I'm in any doubt, it's good artists that remind me that life has abundant meaning and to savour every minute of it. With this in mind, I've never felt I could proclaim myself an artist because to do so would be akin to proclaiming myself to be a god or something, which is a bit much.

2. Because I am struck by the number of dilettante chancers who happily call themselves 'artists' and, were I to do the same, I'd be damned by association; being an 'artist' just doesn't mean what it used to—or maybe it does but I had some naive view that it meant something more. Years ago, at a private view in Liverpool, Tai smashed her wine glass against the wall in response to the pretentious posturing of the paint spattered overall clad neophytes and their half-cocked slushy acrylics. It left a splattered arc of mucky Value Red across the pristine wannabe white cube interior which was easily the best art of the night. Unfortunately the gallerist didn't agree and we were asked to leave. <u>He</u> didn't think we were artists, in fact, he thought we were 'selfish fucking twats'.

3. Because I've never made any money as an artist and have always had to subsidise my art activity with a day job. Financial reward is the only measure of success in any field so in that respect I am a far more successful kerb layer than I am an artist. Therefore, I've always considered myself to be a kerb layer first and an artist second. But I know that I am a better artist than I am a kerb layer. I just <u>am</u> an artist. I think like one <u>all</u> the time. I can turn the kerb laying on and off but I am <u>always</u> an artist. I just can't call myself one. I need to think of a new word

for what I thought 'artist' meant. 'Selfish fucking twat' maybe?

Nat: I was at that private view in Liverpool. He was right, the wine was the best thing in the show.

Family Rubbish #9

A 1977 Topps Chewing Gum football card featuring Willie Carr of Wolverhampton Wanderers. In one corner, the glossy surface is slightly peeling away from the matt red card backing. On the glossy side, Willie is pictured in full colour from the neck up, squinting into the sun, his collar-length hair swept to one side. On the reverse are listed some of his career highlights, vital statistics and, seemingly arbitrarily, a cartoon of Aston Villa full-back Peter Aldis scoring a record breaking headed goal against Sunderland in 1952.

Dom: This was mine! He was one of my favourites. I liked how his hair matched the colour of his shirt. I remember thinking how ace it would be if Wolves only signed players with ginger hair. *Laughs.* We invented a game at junior school in homage to Willie: me, Leebo, Hairy, Holey and Chinny. I can't remember the finer details of the rules but it mainly involved us following the lines of the football pitch and netball court using our willies as joysticks to steer with. It was called Willie Cars.

Nat: Of course it was, well done you!

Dom: And, as was the case with Willie's infamous donkey kick against Everton in 1970, Willie Cars, the game, was also outlawed by the authorities. Mrs Ellis banned it, Mrs Ellis with the blue plastic rimmed glasses and the *Last of the Summer Wine* perm. Shame really, it was a great tribute to a great player."

Family Rubbish #10

The following section is Russell's final entry. Twelve pages from the end of the memo book. The handwriting is sprawling and not easy to read.

Nat does her best to decipher the text:

> Arts festivals: Ugh! They ask you to contribute and you submit an idea based around your art practice and they say "Hmm, not really, we need more jugglers and fire eaters and people on stilts – and something for the kids to do, and maybe hats for dogs," and you think, "Why did they ask me in the first place?" Why not ask a juggler, or a dog milliner or whatever? I still cling to the idea that an art festival is a showcase for artists to share their work and any insight they've gained through making it; a chance for them to justify their existence. But it's not, is it? There might be a couple of headline artists who present their work unencumbered but on the whole everything else has to be accompanied by a sideshow of face paints and people dressed as cartoon characters leading trails through the woods on the lookout for mirror-work crocheted tree-accessories. The quality of any serious art has been sacrificed in favour of an increase in footfall and positive feedback ratings:
>
> "Did the festival meet your expectations, Yes or No?"

"Yes."

"Good!"

No! Not good! Any art experience that meets your expectations has failed. Art should challenge your expectations, that's what art is for, that's what we all went to art college to learn how to do. Arts festivals treat everyone like kids: "But they won't come if there are no rides." Maybe some won't but who cares about them? Nobody will come when all that's left is a dumbed down meaningless cavalcade of interactive party wigs. The worst part is that anyone who comes on spec and might have been interested is given the impression that people playing ukuleles on unicycles is what art is all about and they'll think "Well, that was a load of old horse shit. Why is taxpayers' money being wasted on this?" And they'd be right. And then the penny-pinching government will come along and say "Yes, we hear you, get rid! Get rid of the arts from schools and universities. Get rid of the arts from state funded TV." And by this time the population will be so culturally illiterate they won't even know how shit their lives have become, they'll just sit there in their underpants surrounded by stuffed meerkats, drinking Red Bull and watching *Celebrity Tits* on Sky Arts.

Friday Art Club

A lightweight 1970s hollow core door with a lustrous sapele veneer opens onto a fastidiously clean but spartan back-room office of about three by four metres. The walls are a slightly lighter beige hue than the fitted carpet which was laid thirty years ago but looks brand new. A desk faces away from the door and abuts the far wall below a horizontal slit of a window which is too high to see from. The desk is of a 1980s middle manager style, dark wood veneer on a black plastic-coated box steel frame. The only thing on its surface is an old BT cordless phone, the cables from which hang down the wall to a socket mounted just above the skirting. The only other object in the room is the dark grey polycotton upholstered swivel chair.

Through another sapele doorway sits Mr Weatherburn at a round dark wood dining table with turned spindle legs. He wears a red v-neck golfing sweater and a pair of grey flat front trousers in a low maintenance wool blend. He has a newspaper spread out on the table.

On the radio a famous entrepreneurial disruptor is attempting to validate his business model. He explains how he is disrupting the corporate establishment by using the same techniques that the corporate establishment used to disrupt the corporate establishment that preceded it and which are, in all probability, the same techniques that the corporate establishment before that used to disrupt the corporate establishment that preceded that too. Mr Weatherburn isn't really listening anymore.

Mr Weatherburn closes the paper. Underneath it is a copy of *Britain Yesterday and Today* with a foreword by Peter Sissons which he briefly flicks through before getting to his feet. He wanders into the kitchen, switches off the radio and rinses a mug while he gazes out of the window. In the field at the back he can see a young woman in denim shorts and a vest top cutting down the ragwort with a scythe. He decides to take the dog out for a walk.

Mr Weatherburn takes off his slippers by the front door and then ties the laces of his Clark's Natures, resting each foot in turn on the Saxony cut carpet of the staircase. He fumbles for a dog lead under the navy-blue anorak that hangs from the hooks in the hallway, the sound of which brings Max the Labrador out from the front room.

Mr Weatherburn and Max wander up the unmade track between the thorns and brambles past regular mounds of cut thistle and ragwort. It's warm and the ground is hard. Butterflies flit around the buddleia. The thrum of an approaching vehicle grows steadily louder until birds scatter from the undergrowth and Mr Weatherburn and Max are briefly forced over into the spongy tussock grass at the edge of the path. A group of men in period costume bounce by in a small Mercedes bus on their way to re-enact the Battle of Wakefield in the top field again. Mr Weatherburn holds on to the top stones of the wall for balance on the uneven ground.

Mr Weatherburn continues on his way and as the track widens at the entrance to the community farm, he stops to talk to Mr Davies from the barn conversion on the ridge. They discuss their experiences of electrocardiography –

"It makes your arm twitch, doesn't it?"
and their problems with spam emails –

"I pressed something on the moving around thing on the screen, not the mouse, the other thing, and I put it on something else and now I keep getting emails from people in Bradford asking if I can come and help move some furniture for them."

Max dashes through the heather with Mr Davies's springer spaniel, Jill. Eventually Mr Davies says he has to get off because "her indoors" will be wondering what he's up to.

Mr Weatherburn takes the old cart track up towards the road that circumnavigates the hill with the best views. At the top he hitches Max to the footpath sign and turns to look across the town below while he catches his breath. The chapel, the school, the pub, the engineering works, everything: apple bobbing, Cliff's jumper and the bright orange wax in his ear, Mrs Allen's Wood's Ware and the musty wainscoting, muffled hymns, heavy coats and misty playgrounds, Kicky Hinchliffe, the Ford Anglia, the Hillman Hunter, Dad falling off the ladder at Joe's, Pam on Thursdays in town, working on the DB5 chassis platforms, the office with Brian, Dennis's stories in the canteen, Pam's mum that Christmas, watching Chris play football in the rain, singing Sinatra on the school run with Sarah, the weddings, Danny's first time at the pictures …

The postman pulls up in the squeaky red Peugeot Partner with part of the bumper fastened on with cable ties,
"Mr Weatherburn, I'm glad I've caught you. I've got a parcel for you," the postman hands over a package, "Too big to go through the box."
"Thanks, lad," says Mr Weatherburn, "Much left to do?"
"No, thank God. I've had enough of delivering meerkats and sex toys for one day," says the postman with a pantomime grin and two fingers to his temple like a gun.

Mr Weatherburn sets off again. He climbs the stone stile and joins the narrow footpath across the tussock moor where he lets Max off his lead. A man with a swagger and a grey hoody makes his way in the opposite direction. His dog, a black and tan Jack Russell terrier, catches sight of Max and runs towards him barking aggressively. Max stands his ground, the hair down his back on end. The terrier moves in again but Max fends him off. The stand-off continues and the man in the hoody is running now.

"PEANUT!" he yells, "Peanut!" again, "Peanut!"

By the second Peanut his conviction is on the wane and by the third it is all but smothered by his obvious embarrassment at the dog's name.

"It's okay," shouts Mr Weatherburn, "No harm done. And by the way Peanut is a perfectly good name for a black and tan Jack Russell. Let's shout it together. PEEAANNUTT!" yells Mr Weatherburn at the top of his voice. Peanut and Max look up. "And again," shouts Mr Weatherburn.

"PEANUT!" Both men shout together. Peanut looks quizzical, head cocked. Both men laugh.

"Come on Peanut!" shouts the hoody man again and Peanut runs towards him.

Mr Weatherburn and Max set off down the road in the direction of the shops and Mr Weatherburn can't help smiling as they pass two chubby men in puffa jackets who are having a loud discussion about how much of a dick one of their acquaintances is. The man in the beige jacket says he's "a right dick" and the man in the blue jacket says he's "a total dick."

Mr Weatherburn ties Max to the railings outside the Co-op and goes inside. He ambles along the aisles accompanied by the greatest hits of the 1970s and 80s: *Let's Groove*, Earth Wind & Fire; *China In Your Hands*, T'Pau; *Have You Seen Her?* The

Chi-Lites. He is briefly confused by the newly installed chiller cabinets; the doors open the opposite way to the old ones and he grabs for a non-existent handle. The girl with the glittery make-up points out the problem. She says she did exactly the same thing herself.

In the queue at the checkout, the man in front of Mr Weatherburn is wearing pyjamas and the man behind is humming along to *(I Just) Died In Your Arms Tonight* by Cutting Crew.

"Pop your pin in, buddy," says the young man with the bum fluff beard while Mr Weatherburn is concentrating on not crushing his fish fingers with his potatoes.

On his way out of the shop, Mr Weatherburn pauses at the charity book sale table and puts 50p in the box for the hardback copy of Alec Waugh's *Island in the Sun*, then he scans the small ads on the index cards which are stuck to a cork board with drawing pins. Among the handwritten offers of childcare and gardening services there's "Two female life models required £10.00/hour." To Mr Weatherburn's amusement the contact phone number is only one digit away from his own. He stifles a laugh; he now has an explanation for the strange phone call he received last weekend. He considers this would make an excellent anecdote and he looks around the shop for somebody to tell. He glances back over to the charity book table where the big man with the tattooed neck is leafing through a biography of Donald Wolfit. Mr Weatherburn decides he isn't confident the tattooed neck man would make a very receptive audience; one teatime, a couple of years ago, he had to pull him out of the road where he'd fallen asleep with a half-eaten bag of sweet chilli crisps splayed open on his stomach. In the end Mr Weatherburn decides to leave the shop without mentioning the phone number thing. Perhaps he can tell Sarah about it the next time she rings.

Mr Weatherburn unhitches Max from the railings and they make their way back home the road way. They pass the man walking laps of his small front yard, his arms behind his back and his gaze steadfastly fixed on the middle distance. They pass the offices of the suppliers of aseptic isolation systems, a sign displayed prominently in the window: ON FRIDAYS OUR STAFF HAVE THE RIGHT TO DRESS DOWN. On they go, past the headless pigeon on the pavement outside the newsagent's shop, past the tall man with the wire-rimmed specs who is listening to Bob Marley on speaker-phone, past the closed down shop with the faded sign: HALAL MEAT OFF-LICENCE. They make their way onto the top road where the pavement is adjoined by a high wall for its entire length. Mr Weatherburn finds himself overcome with curiosity. What *is* on the other side of that wall? He must have walked down this street a thousand times and has never thought to find out. He looks down the length of it to see whether there's a lower section he might be able to glimpse over but the wall continues unbroken at its regular height, half a metre above Mr Weatherburn's head. Fifty metres in the distance, just after the big junction box, two large gateposts mark what must have, at one time, been an entrance, but the space between them has been bricked up for as long as Mr Weatherburn can remember. He turns to look back the way he's come and, twenty metres back just after the shop, in amongst the dock leaves and nettles, a fire hydrant marker on a foot high concrete post abuts the base of the wall. Mr Weatherburn pulls Max round and they make their way over. He drops the bag of shopping and Max's lead. "Stay there, lad," he says, and he steps up onto the marker with his right foot. From here he grasps the top of the triangular coping with both hands, wedges the sole of his left shoe into the roughly finished stone of the wall and pulls himself up another half metre or so, his hands shaking with the exertion of maintaining a grip. Then he transfers enough of his weight onto his left foot for just long enough to let go of the coping with his right hand. He swings his elbow over the top, grazing his forearm in the process. He hangs there for a moment while he aligns his varifocals to accurately assess the damage. There's blood, but not too much. Now he heaves his other elbow over, braces both forearms against the far side of the coping and pulls his head and chest above the top of the wall. Both his feet dance around for cracks to settle in. And there, stretching away from him is an unkempt area of broken asphalt, couch grass, brambles and sycamore saplings which Mr Weatherburn recognises as part of the grounds of the hospital that closed down over a decade ago now. "Probably the old car park," he says to himself and he slides down from the wall and dabs at his blooded arm with a pocket handkerchief, it's not as bad as it looks. He picks up his shopping and Max's lead and continues on his way home.

Mr Weatherburn opens the door and unhooks Max who saunters into the front room and flops down in his usual place by the weeping fig. Mr Weatherburn takes off his shoes and then climbs the stairs to the bathroom where he bathes his arm with warm water and TCP. In the kitchen he boils the kettle for a cup of tea and opens a tin of sardines from the Co-op bag. He sits at the table and eats them with a squirt of lemon juice while flicking through *Britain Yesterday and Today*.

Mr Weatherburn spends the afternoon chopping hard boiled eggs to make sandwiches, his contribution to the Lonely Arts Club artists' annual event at the village hall which marks the culmination of a weekend of open studios in the town. This is the sixteenth year that Mr Weatherburn has been involved in some capacity. His wife, Pam had been an accomplished water colourist and he had initially volunteered to show his support of her. He'd help out hanging pictures, building displays and sometimes issuing raffle tickets at the door. As the years had gone by he'd found he got along well with the "arty set." He enjoyed seeing people expressing their creativity. He became more and more involved until he'd found himself chair of the hanging committee.

While Mr Weatherburn was well liked, his promotion to what was in effect the most senior curatorial role in the organisation was seen in some quarters as controversial on account of his lack of any real creative experience. On one memorable occasion, Mr Weatherburn had been embarrassed when he was harangued at a preview evening by Russell Lockwood, one of the artists from the studios in the repurposed old mill. Mr Lockwood had been very unhappy with the hang. He'd also been very drunk and, in Mr Weatherburn's view, extremely rude. In response Mr Weatherburn had maintained his propriety and had simply and calmly explained to Mr Lockwood that his only motivation for accepting the role was his desire to help. The role had needed filling, nobody had put themselves forward and so he'd stepped in. Mr Lockwood had stormed out nevertheless, deliberately smashing Mrs Geldart's stained glass sculpture of a pair of butterflies in the process, an act which earned him a lifetime ban.

Even though most of those gathered had been quick to show their support for Mr Weatherburn, including the other mill artists and certainly the rest of the committee, Pam had seen fit to procure him a generous measure of Scotch to calm his nerves. The whole debacle had unnerved him greatly. He was, and remains to this day, very confused by it.

Ever since Pam died, Mr Weatherburn has preferred to take more of a back seat as far as the annual artists' event is concerned but when called upon he will always make himself available. He recognises how much the arty set did for his wife's confidence and well-being through some difficult times.

At 5pm the landline rings in the office.

"Hello, is that Mr Weatherburn? It's Verity, Mrs Wilkinson, from Art Club. I'm sorry about this, I hope it's not too late, but could you perhaps do cheese sandwiches instead of egg? We're going to have to manage without egg this year with all the concerns about allergies... Better to be safe than sorry."

Mr Weatherburn replaces the handset into its cradle, collects his keys and wallet and reverses the Skoda from the drive. He might just make it back to the Co-op for before it shuts.

Mr Weatherburn returns home with bread, butter, cheese, pickle and a ready-meal shepherds pie for one which he puts in the oven before he gets started. Next, he sets about grating a small mountain of cheese while he half listens to a radio play about Eleanor of Aquitaine. When the pie is cooked, he breaks off for an hour to eat it in front of the television with Max. He catches the second half of the England game while Max lies on his feet.

After the game, a draw, Mr Weatherburn constructs the sandwiches, plates them up under clingfilm and carefully stacks them in the fridge, then he lets Max out into the garden while he washes up and tidies round. He picks up the Co-op bag and realises that he's left the parcel that the postman gave him inside it. He tears open the outer layer of brown paper. Underneath is a belated birthday card and a present from Sarah. *Dad, sorry it's a bit late but I think you'll agree it was worth waiting for x.* Mr Weatherburn opens the next layer of wrapping paper and finds an original 1:24 1965 Airfix kit of an Aston Martin DB5. "Wow" he says to himself as he inspects the artwork on the box, James Bond is dispatching another villain via the car's famous ejector seat.

Mr Weatherburn warms some milk on the hob, fetches Max back inside and makes his way up to bed with his bedtime whisky and his birthday present. The weekend starts now.

The Other Thing Besides

The landline rang early, it was Vincent next door. He was wondering whether Kirsten would be going to the big supermarket. He needed a multi-pack of Devon custard and some Brillo pads. They've stopped doing them at his shop, the smaller supermarket near the bus station. He said "Believe it or not, they haven't got them anymore," and then he said, "I'll pay you with a couple of custards and a Brillo pad" and he reminded Kirsten about the cat food and the other thing besides, what was it now? Tomatoes. And then he thanked Kirsten very much.

Kirsten added Devon custard (four pack) and Brillo pads to the list on her phone and went back to the kitchen where the toast was burning under the grill.

The landline rang again, and this time Kirsten let it go through to the answer phone.

"It's just Vincent again, bothering you. I've found out why Dame Judy wasn't in Cats. I got a double DVD of Lloyd-Webber and all those from when they were making Cats and apparently Dame Judy, a few days before the show went on, was on the stage and her ligament broke, her Achilles tendon in her leg, and she tried to get back a few days after and she was hobbling around and then she fell and that was the end of it. That's when they got you know who. But it wasn't because she had the flu or anything, it was that this happened. I've got a DVD of when they were making it with Andrew Lloyd-Webber but I haven't watched the entire lot of it, it's going on for ages. I was surprised because to begin with Elaine Paige thought she'd had flu or something and her understudy was ill too, but it wasn't that at all, it was Dame Judy's Achilles tendon snapped and she was in hospital and then she tried to get back again and then she fell and that was the end of it just before they were going to open and then Elaine got it. That's all I wanted to tell you."

Kirsten watched from the kitchen window as Vincent shuffled outside in his apron, he was carrying a bottle of turps and a lit cigarette in one hand and unlocking the garage door with the St Christopher keyring key with the other. He disappeared inside for a minute and then reemerged holding a tin of royal blue paint. He'd said he was going to paint his door frame. He rang on the landline yesterday and said he was going to paint the door frame royal blue. He'd said he knew there was a tin in the garage and he hoped there'd be enough. He'd said he wasn't going to Halifax to get the crabs like he usually does because he was going to paint the door frame of the garage instead. Then he said he hadn't seen the owl and he didn't think his sweet peas were going to do very much this year.

Vincent went back inside the house and then came back out without his apron. He broke up some stale bread and sprinkled it onto the bird table then he hung up a pair of socks and the remains of a dish cloth on the washing line.

Kirsten checked the fridge and then made an imaginative sandwich from mainly a tomato for her daughter's school lunch. Out of the kitchen window Vincent had left his garden via the back gate. He didn't have a coat on. Last year, when Vincent's back gate broke, he blamed Kirsten. He said it must have been her because he never used it himself and who else was there? Anyway, he must have only been out to the bins because he wasn't long. He pulled the gate shut very firmly behind him and studied the label on his tin of paint while he finished smoking his cigarette.

Kirsten hurried the kids into the car, edged out into the rush hour and spent the next three hours or so on a visit to the big supermarket via the little and big schools and then back home and then back to the big school again with the forgotten paper-maché homework castle. Actually, after the school run it was the garage for petrol first, and then a week's worth of shopping for the family plus a four pack of Devon custard, some Brillo pads, cat food and the other thing besides which was tomatoes.

Back at home Kirsten unloaded the car and then took the Devon custard, the Brillo pads, the cat food and the tomatoes to Vincent's front door.

"Oh, hello Kirsten," said Vincent, his voice slightly raised so it could be heard above the theme from The Snowman sung by Aled Jones via the Alba hifi system in the front room.

We're floating in the moonlit sky

Vincent thanked Kirsten and then, before she went, insisted she take a look at the cover of the new wrestling DVD he'd been watching.

"Gosh," said Kirsten, turning the case over and inspecting its lively design.

I'm riding in the midnight blue

"Ronda Rousey was there, and they got her up in the ring," Vincent explained. "Triple H weighs about 265 lbs and it's all muscle. Big chap. He's quite famous in wrestling. He's won about everything there is."

Children gaze open mouthed, taken by surprise, nobody down below believes their eyes

"Rock got Ronda Rousey to go up with him, she was in the audience and he stood there and, I mean, Triple H and, er, what the hell's his wife's name? She owns the wrestling, they were going on about how good they were and one thing and another and Ronda Rousey wasn't saying a thing, she was just listening."

We're drifting over icy mountains floating by

"Apparently, she's a big friend of Triple H's. I didn't know, I'd never even heard of her before but apparently, she's famous. And she doesn't look big. Apparently, she's one of the most famous sports people in the world and I didn't know, and she's beat everyone there is to beat."

Suddenly swooping low on an ocean deep, arousing of a mighty monster from its sleep

"Triple H weighs about 265 lbs. He's big. Big, big muscles. He's won about everything there is in wrestling. Ronda Rousey threw him right out of the bloody ring and she doesn't look any bigger than you. She's well-built but she's not fat or anything."

Everyone who sees us greets us as we fly.

Back at home again Kirsten finished putting away the shopping, filled the kettle and put a couple of slices of bread under the grill. Then the landline rang again,

"Here, Kirsten, it's Vincent. I got something for you so when you have a minute, maybe you can pick it up."

Kirsten decided to go straight away so she could get on with some work uninterrupted after lunch. Outside, round the back of the house, it smelt of paint and cigarettes. Vincent showed Kirsten his door frame. He said he'd got up especially early to paint it.

He said, "I said I was going to get up early, didn't I?"

He said he had two tins of paint and he wasn't sure he was going to have enough but in the end he had had enough to do the door as well and he still had a bit left besides. He said his roses were overrun with greenfly and where were all the ladybirds?

"I've got something for you," he said, and he stubbed out his cigarette and dropped it into the empty Cravendale milk carton by the back door. "It's the best there is, Cravendale," he said as he led Kirsten inside. "Here you are, for the shopping," he said, handing Kirsten two cartons of Devon custard and a Brillo pad.

"Thank you," said Kirsten, "You really needn't have."

Then Vincent told Kirsten the story of the time he was out hunting in bear country in Alberta, Canada, the same story he'd told her on Monday. The one where the man drives his station wagon into the ravine and Vincent has to go for help. Not the shorter one where the inexperienced campers pitch their tent near his and are so spooked by the sound of the coyotes that they pack up their things and leave in the middle of the night – the one with the derisive snort after "Those coyotes weren't gonna hurt anybody." Vincent said it was funny how he hadn't thought of this story for years and that it had just come back to him.

When Kirsten got home, she put out another toast fire and remade her lunch. Then she had a bit of a tidy round which meant there wasn't really time to do any work before she had to pick up the kids from school. She edged out into the rush hour and drove to the big school via the little school and then drove back home again via the post office with the birthday card she forgot to send yesterday.

As she opened the front door the landline started ringing. Kirsten let it run onto the answerphone.

"It's Vincent. I forgot to tell you something. It's something you won't believe unless you see it yourself. I couldn't believe it to begin with. I had to go and check myself to make sure I was right …"

The Reception

Paul Wood pulls up between the discarded chest freezer and the Seat Ibiza with the mismatched bumper, opposite the end-terrace where Mr. Iqbal is tending his onions.

"It was supposed to be a crappy day today, wasn't it?" he shouts as he climbs out of the van.

"It's turning out all right, isn't it?" Mr. Iqbal replies with a wave. Mr. Iqbal is standing on the pavement to root out weeds in his garden with a long hoe which he pokes through the iron palings of his fence. His entire front garden is given over to the cultivation of onions. Paul takes a deep breath.

"That smells amazing!"

"Do you want to wait here and I'll get your stuff? A tray of onions, the garlic, ginger and the spices, wasn't it?"

Mr. Iqbal leans his hoe against the gate post and goes into the house while Paul waits on the pavement. A man jogs by wearing an old Huddersfield Town football shirt. His relaxed gait, dark complexion and beard give him the look of Martin Hair from the sports and social club in the 1970s. What happened to Martin Hair? As well as organising the five-a-side football in flared jeans competitions, he was a fell runner of renown.

One race day, Paul stands with his dad outside the house on the edge of the moor waiting for Martin to come down off the tops in a gale. They cheer as he passes. Martin sprints down the lane after the race leader in the pissing rain. Another mile down the valley, he overhauls him. There's a smudgy halftone picture of Martin with his winner's medal in the local paper. Another time, Paul and his dad give Martin a lift home from a race and the door of the old Peugeot 104 comes open as they drive along Hill Top Road. Martin's coat falls out and a wagon from the quarry runs it over.

Mr. Iqbal comes back outside carrying the tray of onions, garlic, ginger and spices. Paul opens the doors of the Transit Connect and Mr. Iqbal slides it into the loadspace.

Back on the road, Paul waits at the zebra crossing by the bowling greens in the park where two men in hi-vis vests are marshalling members of the Siberian husky club across the road. Dozens of men and women in puffa coats and tight jeans file through the gates, some with as many as six dogs in their charge.

At the lights on the main road, Paul sits in traffic again. This time he is outside the Red Lion pub where a group of pasty-faced men in sun-bleached anoraks huddle around the doorway smoking cigarettes.

On his nineteenth birthday, Paul is followed into the toilets of the Red Lion by half a dozen members of a gang of local football casuals. He is accused of standing on the toe of the one in the Tacchini tracksuit top while he was fetching drinks from the bar. Paul doesn't remember the incident but concedes it may have happened without his realising; he is quite drunk. He apologises and attempts a self-deprecating joke about being clumsy and not competent to negotiate the busy bar in his new and unfamiliar birthday trainers. He dodges the first punch but the second and third connect solidly. He notices the strip-light glinting off a chunky silver watch strap as he hits the floor. He curls up with his face to the wall and endures a brief ritualised kicking before the sound of a commotion in the bar distracts his assailants and they rush to investigate. Paul climbs to his feet gingerly. His face stings. He washes blood from a split lip and a cut above his eye before cautiously peering around the door into the bar. The pub has cleared out, only the confused-looking staff remain; one of them is nursing similar looking injuries to Paul's own. The big table in the corner has been turned over and there's broken glass everywhere. Paul makes his way outside. The street is quiet too, everyone has disappeared, including his friends. It's late but he can still catch the last bus, so Paul makes his way through the town centre, nervously crossing the street at any sign of potential trouble. He dabs at his cuts with the sleeve of his jacket, the one above his eye is still bleeding heavily, he knows he must look a state. At the entrance to the bus station, where the light fans out across the pavement, Paul leans hard on the greasy glass door and pushes his way into the glowing hangar of an interior with its distinctive aroma of cigarettes and disinfectant. He casts his eye down the long row of stands to where his bus will arrive and there, making themselves conspicuous through a range of anti-social activities, are his attackers.

Paul doesn't hang around, he leaves the bus station and rings home from one of the phone boxes outside. He knows his dad will be in bed, he starts at the bakery at 5am. There's a scratchy "Hello," and a "Bloody hell, mate, I've got work in the morning," but his dad agrees to drive out to pick him up.

Paul sets off walking, and forty minutes later, as he's crossing the bridge over the canal, he spots his dad idling at the lights. He legs it across the road, ducks into the passenger seat and pulls the door shut behind him, enclosing himself in the warm shell of the van.

"Bloody hell, mate!" says his dad again. "What happened? Are you okay?"

The van smells of the van, of the bakery and bread and home.

"I've felt better," says Paul, inspecting his face in the vanity mirror. It's a mess.

"Bloody hell, let's get you home and get you cleaned up."

"Thanks, Dad. Sorry I woke you up."

"Bloody hell, don't worry about that, look at the state of you!"

As the adrenaline and the alcohol subside, Paul's bruises begin to throb. The engine thrums, the dashboard glows and Paul's dad calls the football hooligans "A bunch of fucking ignorant little twats." Paul's never heard him say 'fucking' or 'twats' before.

Back outside the Red Lion thirty years later, the lights change, and Paul pulls away, leaving the bleached out anorak men to their Superkings. He turns off the main road, down through the underpass, and then left onto the bumpy unmade track of the industrial estate. The van bounces through the big puddle that Peter from Village Green Grocers has been meaning to sort out since it got bad last winter.

"Sorry about that, Paul," Peter shouts as Paul pulls up in front of the roller shutter doors, "I've been meaning to get that seen to."

"No harm done," says Paul as he climbs out of the van.

"Right then, lad. What are you after? How many folk do you reckon you've got coming?"

Peter and Paul discuss arrangements for the reception; who's coming and what's on the menu. Californication by the Red Hot Chili Peppers plays over the old paint spattered Toshiba radio hanging from two upside-down wire coat hangers on pulleys above the parsnips. At one point, Peter breaks off from their discussion and points to it,

"That used to be your dad's," he says.

"Did it? Don't remember that," says Paul.

"Aye, I think he had it in the back of the shop. He gave it me a few years ago when mine packed up."

104

Paul is conscious of how much he's got to prepare and wary of Peter's ability to sustain a conversation, so he cuts things short. He hedges his bets and just takes a couple of standard large boxes of mixed fruit and veg' – minus the onions and the garlic. He pays with cash.

"Thanks, lad. I'll see you on Thursday. Love to the others."

Fifty yards down the track, Paul pulls up outside Alice's unit.

"Hiya, love. How's it going?" she asks.

"Getting there," says Paul.

As they load boxes of wine and beer into the van, they reminisce about the sports and social club. They straggle across the moors on disobedient ponies in the 1980s.

"Just let your pony pick its own way!" shouts the horse lady with the RP voice and a taste for roll-ups as they navigate the steep stoney path down to the river bank. That's when Alice sets off down the valley and isn't seen again for nearly an hour.

"Where on earth have you been?" says the horse lady.

"I was letting my pony pick its own way," explains Alice, a bit flustered.

Later, out on the open moor, Paul's dad decides he needs to piss, so the horse lady halts the convoy while he dismounts and sets off in search of a suitable spot. There's nothing but windswept moor grass for miles around. The horse lady dismounts and rolls herself a cigarette. Paul's dad walks fifty yards then turns to look back. All eyes are on him, both human and equine, there's nothing much else to look at. He walks on another fifty yards and turns again. Other riders have begun to dismount. Another fifty yards; they're still watching and now someone is passing round refreshments. Another fifty yards; they are opening foil wrapped sandwiches. Once Paul's dad is happy with the distance he's put between himself and his fellow trekkers, he undoes his fly and relieves himself, prompting cheers and much applause from his audience.

Paul thanks Alice for the drinks and they hug their goodbye.

Back out onto the ring road, past the luxury carpets at affordable prices, the reclamation yard, the gearbox services, the paper converters, the polythene extruders, the hand car wash and the bridal make-up salon. Paul swings the van left by the old mill and in less than half an hour, he's out in the hills, rattling over cattle grids on single track roads. He follows a small peloton of cyclists up towards the farm.

Paul's about eleven years old when he's riding Christine Bowden's bike in the lane outside the house on the edge of the moor. Malcolm, the farmhand with the rubbish homemade tattoos, careers over the cattle grid much too quickly in his stupid Ford Escort with the wide wheel arches. He's on his way home from dipping sheep in the tub outside the big new Atcost barn. Paul has to throw himself into some nettles to get out of the way. He's upset and he goes inside to find his dad is also upset because some of the sports and social kids have etched the name of a local punk band into Paul's mum's new rose pattern place mats.

When Paul reaches the farm, the weather has turned and a fine rain has begun to squall. He winds down his window.

"I'm here for the chickens!" He shouts to Christine Bowden who is on a quad bike in the bottom field with her poodle, Marcel. Christine points up the track, signalling for Paul to follow her and they set off up the hill towards the barn at the top. The wind sweeps Berlioz's *La Damnation de Faust* Paul's way from the old Sanyo radio cassette player which Christine has wrapped in polythene and strapped to her mudguard with thick black PVC tape. They pull up next to each other in the yard and head into the barn to fetch the chickens. Marcel follows them inside.

"Do you remember Malcolm who worked here years ago?" Paul asks.

"Yes. Why?"

"I was just thinking about the time he ran me into that patch of stinging nettles."

"Don't remember that. Sounds like something he'd do though."

"What happened to him?"

"Fuck knows."

"Wasn't he into all that battle reenactment stuff?"

"I don't know, was he?" smirks Christine. "He was in that shit band."

"Weren't we all," says Paul.

They load up the chickens and a couple of dozen eggs and Christine disappears back down the hill with Marcel, trailing Berlioz in their wake.

In the lane there is bird shit, a scattering of sycamore keys, acorns, a crushed snail, a burst slug, a fluffy green ball of moss and a torn face mask. There are petals from a flower garden, bedraggled feathers, lichen encrusted twigs, red berries and a slimy porridge of leaves lining the gutter.

From up here on the valley side, Paul can see the house on the edge of the moor and he can smell the damp cupboards and coal dust. There's ice on the inside of the windows, heavy horsehair upholstery with laddered nylon covers, and a television set which only tunes to a snowy Yorkshire TV with no vertical hold.

One rough day when the oak tree in the garden is tapping on the bedroom window, Paul's dad finds a tramp asleep in the scullery. He loses his temper and throws him out. They've seen the tramp around before, always in the same old threadbare woollen suit with bulging pockets, trousers held up with bailing twine, his knackered black slip-on shoes lined with polythene. Paul's mum says he looks like Ilie Năstase fallen on hard times with his long lank hair and stubble. Paul's dad says he feels bad for having got so angry.

"He's not really doing anyone any harm," he says, but he knows Paul and his sister are scared, so he starts locking the scullery up after that.

There's a chilly wind and it's only six degrees according to the temperature gauge on the dashboard of the van. Small birds flit from one side of the road to the other, from the bird feeders on the new estate back to the hedgerows on the edge of the pasture. Back and forth.

At the abandoned farmhouse, a Robin looks out through the mucky window from the back of a heavy looking wooden chair in the front room.

Leaves are blowing uphill and the rain turns heavy. Paul climbs into the van, puts on the sidelights and sweeps away debris with the wipers. His ears are cold.

Years ago, in the back room on the first floor of the bakery, Paul sits by the window and traces pictures of footballers from an old magazine onto the backs of paper bags while the wind throws rain against the glass. He's out of the weather and out of the way. His dad is downstairs in the shop, he's been up even earlier than usual preparing a hundred Eccles cakes for the man who looks like Terry Nutkins who drives here from miles away. Paul's dad is an accomplished and meticulous baker, and the shop is well known. People come all the way from as far as Leeds and Bradford.

Paul arrives at Mr Birkhead's and pulls the van up on the drive of the modernised interwar dormer bungalow. He climbs out and crosses the plastic lawn to the new grey composite front door. Mr Birkhead officially retired some years ago but has never really managed to draw a line under his career as an importer of some of the finest ingredients from Northeast Asia. He's maintained contact with a favoured handful of suppliers and customers, to the relief of both.

As he makes his way up the resin bound driveway, Paul instinctively makes a grab for a falling leaf. He catches it and shoves it into his pocket.

A long time ago, on a blustery autumn day by the river at Kirkby Lonsdale, Paul and his dad invent a game they call Leaves: they give themselves five minutes to catch as many falling leaves as they can. It's surprisingly difficult and they rarely catch more than one or two each. After they finish playing, Paul keeps the leaves he's caught. He can't just throw them back onto the ground to rot away into the soil where they came from. He keeps them in his pockets even though they inevitably crumble to dust there and finish up under his finger nails when he reaches in to retrieve his loose change.

Busy part-time Oriental food wholesaler and one half of an Everly Brothers tribute act, Mr. Birkhead has installed a new moulded plastic water feature as the centre piece of his fake lawn. A trio of life-sized otters are frozen mid-frolic among a series of pretend rocks. He's not got the water flowing through it yet, but he's had a lot on.

It's along a section of the River Lune in Kirby Lonsdale that Paul and his dad see a pair of wild otters, a hundred yards or so upstream of Devil's Bridge—so called because the devil himself built it in return for the soul of the first person to cross it, of course. The otters play and swim and are unfazed by the small audience that gathers to watch.

Inside the house, Mr. Birkhead demonstrates both his new app controlled flush-mounted flame effect electric fire in light mineral grey and the Phil Everly signed Gibson J-180 which is mounted in a perspex case on the wall beside it. Paul has been introduced to the guitar on most of his previous visits but is too polite to mention it. Eventually, Mr. Birkhead leads him through the house and out into the back garden where an excitable Weimaraner greets them with a deflated football attached to a tooth. Mr. Birkhead unhooks the ball and throws it away from the large shed over to which he leads Paul. Inside the shed, the shelves that run from floor to ceiling along three sides of the interior are crammed with dumplings, noodles, kimchi, teas and juices.

The cloud thins and the weather brightens again. Paul loads his groceries into the van. His mind wanders back to the house on the edge of the moor where his dad draws the fire by holding a copy of the Sun across the aperture of the fireplace. The only reason Paul's dad buys a newspaper is for lighting a fire. He's not bothered about the news. He buys the Sun because it's the cheapest. Paul sometimes catches him reading bits of articles while he's doing this, it's the only time he ever sees him read the paper. If the fire is still reluctant, he asks Paul to fetch a block of smelly firelighters from the top shelf in the scullery. Paul has to stand on the mop bucket to reach them.

At the temporary traffic lights where they're digging up the road, Paul winds down his window to let in some air and de-mist the van. The Northern Gas Networks men are discussing what to have for lunch. All four of them have decided on ham salad on white without beetroot. The one in the beanie hat who is sitting astride a little caterpillar digger is having extra mayo with his.

The one with his hard hat over his hood is going to fetch their order from the Betts Bakery on the main road. A Makita site radio is playing Get the Party Started by Pink.

Paul takes the back roads to the village, past bramble verges and the little grey pony that must be a hundred years old now. Past the quarter full bottle of Lambrini next to the bench with the big view and past the pair of crows who are eating a flattened squirrel. Paul stops on the blind bend by Mrs. Walker's old house and reverses to let an E-Type Jaguar through. The driver briefly acknowledges Paul by extending the fingers of his right hand from the steering wheel without entirely letting go.

On the edge of the village, Paul stops to let a young couple in walking gear cross the road, they drop crisps for their Border terrier who doesn't take his eyes off them. On, past the old police station, the swimming baths, the primary school and into the narrow streets of hiking shops and cafés. Paul noses the van through a gaggle of primary colour clad hikers and pulls the van into the small yard at the back of the bakery. He parks up in front of the goal posts his dad initially painted on the wall in the early 80s. They were touched up a couple of times in the 90s but they're fading now behind a stack of old bread trays and a drift of leaves. Paul switches off the ignition. The onions in the loadspace have given a twist to the van's signature aroma of fresh bread. The slow creak of the clutch pedal under Paul's foot connects him with the dead space of the van's interior. He squints as a brief shaft of sunlight breaches the visor. He shifts in his seat and the dull rustle of synthetic fibres fills the space inside and outside his head. His eyes are lost in the dusty surface of the dashboard, his ears in the regular tick tick tick of the cooling engine.

The Man with the Fashionable Hairstyle

The man with the fashionable hairstyle leaves the house. He waves to the woman in the kitchen window who is eating handfuls of Sainsbury's Raspberry Crunch cereal straight from the box. He fixes a pair of ear buds into his ears and sets off down the street on foot. Behind the fence, on the allotments, a girl of about ten years of age holds a glass of yellow smoothie in one hand and a newt in the other. She carries them both over to a small wooden shed where she sets down the smoothie and drops the newt into an orange bucket with all the others. A ginger cat watches with interest from a branch of a garrya. The girl scoops up a handful of soil and sprinkles it over the newts, then she picks up the bucket and exits the allotments ahead of the man with the fashionable hairstyle. The girl sets off along the path to the estate. She skirts round to the bottom house where she knocks on the front door and waits. The man with the fashionable hairstyle is about twenty metres behind her.

An elderly man answers the door and shows the girl through the house to the back garden where there's a small pond guarded by a plastic heron. Together, they release the newts into the pond.

The elderly man's house is dingy, the front room is dominated by an enormous three-piece suite of which only the chair in front of the television has seen much wear. There's a tear in the chintz upholstery, straggles of frayed fabric where the cat likes to scratch, and the antimacassar over the back is stained brown. Balanced on the arm of the chair is an ashtray and a hardback copy of Nana Mouskouri's heavy looking memoir, on the floor below that, a wastepaper basket contains several empty Seabrook cheese and onion crisp packets. The room is decorated with several framed photographs of big cats, mainly tigers but also several lions, a few "magnificent leopards" and one or two cheetahs:

"Have you ever heard a cheetah purr?"

"No," says the girl.

"I have, on the radio in Greece," says the man and he hands the girl a bowl of ripe cherry tomatoes to take home with her. She puts one in her mouth as she walks back down the path.

"Thank you!"

The man with the fashionable hairstyle is down by the railway bridge now. It's a cool but pleasant day, the trees are green and there's a bit of colour here and there: honeysuckle, foxgloves and that white stuff from Harlow Carr.

"What's that white stuff we got from Harlow Carr?" Asks the woman who is leaning on the door frame with a mug of tea in her hand.

"Which?" Says the man with the bucket hat and the slight stammer who is crouched over the water feature he's installing; a glazed ceramic ball in a bed of blue slate chippings.

"The one we put in the back, in front of the big prickly thing."

"Astrantia?"

"That's it! I can never remember. Anyway, it's coming out."

"Oh good."

"The buddleia's a way off yet though, you cut it back too hard."

The man with the fashionable hairstyle passes the fridge, the child's bicycle and the big section of brown faux leather modular seating that has been dumped on the pavement outside the telephone box where the man with the full-length trench coat and skinny roll-ups goes to read his hefty paperbacks when it's raining.

Back at home, the newt girl leaves the tomatoes on the table in the kitchen next to the halved lemon on the willow pattern plate her mum bought from a charity shop. In the allotment, a large fly has drowned in her smoothie.

On the road around the park, the man with the fashionable hairstyle is passed every ten seconds or so by the tired looking participants of a running event. There's a series of orange ribbon route-markers tied to lampposts, trees and street signs. The runners wear Get Your Rush On T-Shirts, running tights, compact backpacks, fluorescent trainers and Vegetarian Cycling & Athletic Club hoodies. A woman in a vest top with the number 141 attached to the back grabs the arm of the tall male runner next to her and pulls sharply to guide him around the dog muck on the pavement. The runners straggle past the community centre where the chairs have been stacked and pushed to the edges of the hall. A table tennis player with an Eastern European accent is angrily stripping the rubbers from his bat after a heavy defeat.

"Fuck this fucking fuck!"

The man with the fashionable hairstyle looks up briefly as the table tennis player storms out of the building, his hastily stowed towel trailing from an unzipped sports bag.

Further along the street at the Cloud 9 vape store, there's an offer on their Nasty Fix Disposable Pod Systems: Pineapple lemonade, Blackcurrant cotton candy, Cushman mango, Watermelon ice, Menthol, Asap grape, Double Apple, all the flavours.

A blue VW Polo pulls up outside a terraced houses and a woman with bright red streaks in her hair climbs out with a bunch of carnations and roses. The man with the fashionable hairstyle pauses as she crosses the pavement in front of him. She knocks at the door of number 14 and lets herself in. She edges her way down the hallway which is lined along one side with bulk bought dog food systems, and along the other with excess boxes of chocolates and biscuits, some dating from as long as three Christmases ago. In the kitchen she arranges the flowers in a glass jug, lets the old Labrador into the back garden and makes a start preparing the food. In the front room, a man in his seventies glances up briefly from his laptop. He's wearing a pair of off-the-peg reading glasses on the end of his nose and a t-shirt featuring the slogan Stop Fucking Killing People You Twats. He is composing a Facebook post outlining his admiration for NHS workers and his disdain for the Conservative Party.

"How do you do a rainbow emoji?" he shouts through to the kitchen.

The man with the fashionable hairstyle continues on his way over the storm drain which is pink with cherry blossom, past the house with the life-size statue of a sheep on the plastic lawn, past the twenty-foot-long hopscotch chalked onto the pavement, past dandelions, past graffitied lampposts, past the house with the empty picture frames on the windowsill, past the rubberised glove in the road, past the PARKING £1 spray-painted on the crumbling render of the mostly demolished warehouse.

The sun burns through the clouds to dapple the asphalt, it brings out a grey haired man in welly shoes and frayed flannels into his garden.

"Morning!" he says to the man with the fashionable hairstyle.

"Morning!" he says to the woman in the purple anorak who is just passing with a parlour palm in a Jack Fulton Frozen Food bag.

The man bends down and picks off a large snail from the side of his water butt. He throws it into the road where it is immediately crushed by the oncoming 87 bus.

"They're such a pain at the moment, aren't they?" says the woman.

"I know, look at the state of my hollyhocks," says the man.

"My hostas are the same. I've ended up stringing a line between the house and the shed and I hang them off it in pots until they get established. Even then, I know as soon as I plant them out, they'll be besieged," says the woman.

"Blimey, there's commitment!" Says the man.

"I know! I don't even like hostas."

The man with the fashionable hairstyle decides to cut through the subway across from the sports centre, past the dirty pink and white tiles and the graffiti: WE ARE MANY THEY ARE FEW. He passes a small group of people with wet hair and swimming bags. The tall dark haired man in the yellow t-shirt and the woman in the gold rimmed specs are discussing the early 90s music scene. Another man, who is wearing a Manchester United shirt, says he doesn't know much about music.

"I only know about football," he says.

"Do you remember Right Said Fred?" says the woman.

"I'm Too Sexy?" says the tall man.

"They were gay," says the football man.

The tall man and the woman in the glasses start singing.

"I'm too sexy for my shirt ..."

"They were gay, them," says the football man.

"I'm so sexy it hurts," sing the others.

"They were gay, them," says the football man again.

"I'm too sexy for your party ..." sing the others.

"They were gay," says the football man.

"I'm a model, you know what I mean and I do my little turn on the catwalk ..."

"They were gay, them."

After contributing "They were gay" nine times the football man starts singing himself

"Deep deep dippy dippy dippy dip ..." and the other two move the discussion on to Whitney Houston.

The man with the fashionable hairstyle pulls his phone from his pocket to swap playlists.

He's behind two women in their fifties as he reemerges from the subway into the sunshine. The women turn right, down towards the sports centre.

"Me and Darren are off to Chatsworth at the weekend," says the one on the left with the blonde ponytail. "We're meeting some old friends of ours. We first met them in Ibiza in 1991 and we've stayed friends ever since but they live in Derby, so we're meeting up at Chatsworth."

"Oooh, I *LOVE* Chatsworth!" says the woman on the right with the enormous holdall over her shoulder.

"I don't know where it is, I've never been."

"You just go straight down the M1, just follow the signs."

"How long do you think it'll take us to get there?"

"I'd give yourselves a good hour, maybe an hour and a half in case there's any road works."

"How far off the motorway is it?" says the ponytail woman, sounding a bit anxious.

"I don't know, I've never been," says the woman who loves Chatsworth.

"I thought you said ..." starts ponytail woman, but she's interrupted.

"What's that on your leg?" the woman who loves Chatsworth says, pointing to some black strapping around the ponytail woman's left leg.

"Oh that, Andy Murray invented it to protect his ankle while he plays tennis, I use it for Zumba."

The man with the fashionable hairstyle cuts through the car park of mainly Audis and continues on past the Sikh temple. He passes another discarded fridge outside the newsagent's shop with the anti-ram bollards around the cash machine. Next to it, an elderly man stops to talk to an elderly woman.

"Give my regards to Derek, won't you," he says, "not that he'll remember who I am."

"He doesn't even know who *I* am," says the woman. "He calls me Elsie, *that* was his mother's name."

The man with the fashionable hairstyle excuses his way past, then cuts through the precinct where the Italian restaurant, the bakery, the haberdashery, the women's clothes shop and the estate agent used to be. It's empty now, apart from a pop-up shop selling discount luggage and a man feeding some pigeons. On to the pedestrianised bit outside the municipal art gallery where early 2000s chart hits dribble out from some speakers suspended from the overhanging roof. A woman with an enormous canvas tote bag is struggling with the heavy smoked glass doors of the gallery entrance. Inside, a couple in their sixties stare up at a large Victorian painting of a muscular woman in a shiny purple dress and a crown of oak leaves, she's running a tiger through with a long sword while a mother and her baby lie dead on the floor.

"Nice bit of imperialist propaganda there," says the man.

The woman leans in to examine the notes printed on the A6 piece of white foam board next to the painting.

"Ooh, it's Britannia!" She exclaims, "She's a *big lass*, isn't she!"

Outside the newsagent's, a young woman in a stripy top and plastic-rimmed glasses points to the newspapers on the stand

and says to an older woman in a big, quilted anorak, "Look, Mum, there's that guy who got stabbed in the eye, they stabbed him straight in the eye."

The man with the fashionable hairstyle skips down the steps onto the path through the small grassy area planted with daffodils and tulips. On the bench, facing the big Ann Summers shop, two women sit while a little girl flicks through a picture book.

"I'm just so tired of spam and junk mail," explains the one in the vintage swing coat. "I know I shouldn't obsess over it but there comes a point where I get so weary of ignoring it that it becomes less aggravating to just give in and let it ruin my day."

"God, I know!" says her companion. "It's like a small child tugging at your sleeves and mithering. Except, with a small child, when it gets too much, you can get down to their level, tell them to be quiet and explain that you're short on cash, so you're not going to waste it on useless crap no matter how much they pester. You can't do that with these people, it just keeps coming and coming, all day every day for the whole of your life until you die."

"Look, Geoff, Cola Cubes!" says the woman in the puffa coat to the man also in a puffa coat outside the sweet shop.

The man with the fashionable hairstyle is at the crossing by the supermarket now. The lights change and he steps out into the road. A woman with dyed pink hair and a Blondie t-shirt is crossing from the opposite side. She's talking to her companion, a woman in a billowing black outfit in jersey.

"Sometimes I daren't even touch them 'cause I know I'm gonna get a shock," she says, and she mimes getting a static shock from a shopping trolley. "Eeurggharghh!"

A man in a grey fleece jacket skips around the Blondie woman with his head down and the man with the fashionable hairstyle has to swerve slightly to avoid him.

The clouds have completely cleared now and the man with the fashionable hairstyle takes out a pair of dark sunglasses and slides them onto his nose. He adjusts his ear buds and continues on his way past some elderly women on their way to Primark.

"I promised our Tony I'd get him some boxers."

Outside Poundland, the man with the fashionable hairstyle passes a man in a fleece jacket who is singing to himself quite loudly.

"*I need some love like I've never needed love before, I wanna make love to ya baby ...*"

The man with the fashionable hairstyle hurries on, past a young woman with blonde highlights and contouring who is saying she can't do Tuesday because she's got to pick up her fucking dry cleaning. On, past the woman in the bug-eye sunglasses and waterfall cardigan who is saying she has literally *no* idea.

Outside the town hall, the man with the fashionable hairstyle edges through the crowd of regional bandsmen who have gathered there during a break in the championships to smoke and vape and eat and chat.

"Sorry, lad. Am I in your way?"

The driver's door of the silver Ford Focus opens and the bad-tempered table tennis player gets out. He's not bad tempered anymore, he's all smiles. He locks the car door and wanders down towards the supermarket with his phone to his ear,

"Oh my God, that's good good news. Thank you thank you, this is such a relief."

The man with the fashionable hairstyle passes a group of teenagers in trainers, hooded tops and baseball caps. They hold skateboards under their arms and they chew their earphone cables.

On through town, the man with the fashionable hairstyle turns right under the 1960s cantilevered roof, past the big lunchtime men with their enormous sandwiches and shirts.

"How much did you get for the Audi?"

"Seven and a half."

A woman with her glasses on a chain around her neck is smoking a cocktail cigarette while she drinks coffee outside Café Culture.

"Long time no see, Roy! Where's your shopping?" she shouts to a man who is also wearing a pair of glasses on a chain around his neck. He's standing outside the travel agent's where he's been contemplating a Festive Getaway to Florence (From just £209 per person—guided city walking tour included). Before he has a chance to reply, the woman accidentally drops her cigarette and jumps out of her seat to brush the hot ash from her distressed jeans.

"Oops! Y'all right, Cheryl love?" he says.

"Yes, no harm done," says the woman, checking her cigarette for dirt. "Hey, you've got your glasses on a chain like mine. It's so much easier, isn't it?"

"Aye, I always know exactly where they are. Very handy!" says the man, slipping his specs onto his nose and peering at her over the top of them. "Ready for anything!"

One of the big lunchtime men wipes his mouth with the back of his wrist, screws his sandwich bag into a tight ball and throws it in roughly the direction of a bin. The man with the fashionable hairstyle absentmindedly kicks it along a bit further and it comes to rest on the stone setts next to a discarded Ikea customer service note: Dear customer, I would be happy to hear your opinion of the store. What is good? What could be better? Please write down your thoughts. They will help us improve. Underneath this printed section is some handwritten bubble writing in pencil: Kati ♥'s prison & court.

The red-haired postman is emptying the big pillar box outside the empty shop unit where the woman with the striped tracksuit top is discussing the price of public transport with the tall man with the old fashioned mac and the bag-for-life.

"It's free to Howarth on the bus and I enjoy the journey, it's £20 to Blackburn on the train," she explains.

The man sets down his bag, holding it upright between his ankles. He hoicks up his trousers and adjusts his unusual rimless glasses.

"It's absolutely ridiculous," he says. "It costs £2.60 on the bus into town from my house. I can walk it in 20 minutes. It takes nearly that long on the bus anyway by the time it's gone round the houses."

Under a low cloud of weed smoke, a group of young men with an aggressive looking bow-legged terrier are huddled around the top of the steps down to the lower precinct. The man with the fashionable hairstyle skirts around them and takes the steps two at a time. One of the young men is staring up at the pigeons as, in splendid unity, they fly around the square again and again before returning to settle on the parapet of Superdrug.

"They love doing that, don't they?" he says.

He stiffens, takes a deep breath and yells out to the flock as they swoop overhead.

"Last one back's a cunt!"

Two young women come out of the eccentric looking shop with the window display featuring four tins of salmon paste, two bottles of Mateus Rosé, a single lightbulb, a nine pack of toilet paper and three tabby cat scraper foil art kits. They're talking as they pass the man with the fashionable hairstyle.

"Bloody hell, remind me never to go in there again."

"*I told you!*"

"*I know*, I should have listened."

Inside the shop, the elderly proprietor is talking to a young man with a shaved head through a forest of faded advertisements.

"The world's gone mad. It's not England anymore," he says as he ducks behind the counter to retrieve a plastic box full of tangled phone chargers. Through the open doorway behind him is a gloomy threadbare interior; a heat-stained gas fireplace, a spilled open record case, an electric organ for playing a medium shuffle potpourri on.

"It's like when I go round to my friend's house, it's the same round there, you know? He's from a middle-class family, plenty of money, but when you go round there now, there's stuff everywhere. He just doesn't care and I don't understand why ..."

The proprietor flicks his side parting back into place and pushes one of the phone chargers towards his customer.

"No, it's like this," says the young man, pulling a cable out of his pocket and holding up the plug.

The proprietor ducks behind the counter again, vocalising a small exhalation as he delves into the box of chargers. He continues talking from the restricted crawl space under the counter top even though his chin is forced against his chest, half trapping his voice in the back of his throat and giving it the timbre of a medieval bladder pipe.

"He's got a dog that bites your arm off as soon as you walk through the door. The house is rented because he lost all his money. His daughter goes out with her backside on show and he just thinks it's funny. Things were never like this before. It's like living in a different country."

The proprietor resurfaces clutching another charger. He rearranges his side-parting and in his normal voice says,
    "How about this one?"
The young man inspects it,
    "No, like this," he says, holding up the plug again ...

Outside, the man with the fashionable hairstyle has crossed the ring road. He's passed a noisy pair of crows in a rowan tree and the hand-painted sign staked into the grass verge outside the chip shop: ATTENTION: DiD YOU SEE A GrEEN CAr PArKED HErE ON friDAY 23rd JAN CALL 07700 900450 rewArD.

A man with long grey hair, a beard, and a wide-brimmed leather hat is unloading a pair of Victorian wooden trestles from the back of a twelve-year-old Peugeot Partner. He's berating himself for having bought them.
    "It really indicates the state of my mental ... um, state doesn't it?" He says to the woman in the striped fleece jacket and woollen beanie hat who is helping him.

The woman suggests the trestles might make nice standard lamps. The long-haired man says they won't.

Someone is playing Bad Company songs and there is laughter coming from the launderette.

The bins are out for bin day so the man with the fashionable hairstyle has to slalom around them on the pavement as he makes his way along the terraces to the canal. The woman with the tie-dyed, mirror-work bag with tassels on it says the school isn't big enough, she says they need to build a bigger one. The man in the army surplus jacket is agreeing with her.

The builders who are digging up a lawn to replace it with a new resin-bound driveway are listening to Tom Grennan's *A Little Bit of Love* on a loud site radio. Next door, there's a dog barking and at the house opposite, a man in Crocs is cutting a cypress hedge with a noisy hedge trimmer. Further along, a short man in his seventies with thick plastic-rimmed glasses is talking on speaker phone in his garden.

"I'm not going anywhere, I'm still waiting for my new jockey wheel. Keith still hasn't sent it."

There's a blackbird singing in a sycamore tree above the Nerf gun bullets in the gutter.

A cyclist in dark glasses and lycra rounds the corner into the street and the man with the fashionable hairstyle waves to him as he passes.

At the end of the road, a group of young children are sitting on a steep rocky outcrop watching somebody in a beekeeper's outfit pumping smoke into a hive.

Two middle aged men with binoculars around their necks are talking.

"I'm pretty sure that was a wheatear."

"I didn't get a good enough look."

The man with the fashionable hairstyle passes them as he takes the short cut through the field to the back of the house. He swings open the garden gate, pockets his earbuds and knocks on the door. While he waits for a reply, he takes off his sunglasses and scrolls through the menus on his phone. The door is eventually opened by a man in a fashionable t-shirt.

"Hey, how you doing? What you been up to?" he says.

"Oh, nothing," says the man with the fashionable hairstyle.

Acknowledgements

Nothing would ever happen without Georgia, Molly and Edie, they are the best.

Many *many* thanks to David Collard, all the Leapers in the Dark and the Carthorse Orchestra for their support and inspiration throughout the dreary lockdown years of 2020–2022. The prospect of another of our online gatherings got me through some dark days.

And thanks of course to Kevin, Hetha, Leonora, Lin, and all at Bluemoose for putting this together.